# THE GREAT BIG BOOK OF GAMES AND PUZZLES

# THE GREAT BIG BOOK OF GAMES AND PUZZLES

ARCTURUS

ARCTURUS

This edition published in 2008 by Arcturus Publishing Limited
26/27 Bickels Yard, 151–153 Bermondsey Street,
London SE1 3HA

Copyright © 2006 Arcturus Publishing Limited

ISBN: 978-1-84193-467-9

Printed in Singapore

*Design and Illustration by* CREATIVE QUOTIENT

Compiler: Anna Amari-Parker
Editor: Rebecca Gerlings

# Contents

# Party Games ════════════════════════════ 71-90

# Guessing Games ════════════════════════ 91-106

# Hand Games ═══════════════════════════ 107-124

# Paper and Pencil Games ══════════════════ 125-136

# Word Games

# Strategy Games

# Tabletop Games

# Card Games

# Dice Games

# THE GREAT BIG BOOK OF GAMES AND PUZZLES

Whether you're looking for party games, rainy day activities
or brainteasers, you're sure to find what you're after in
**The Great Big Book of Games and Puzzles**.

All entries begin with a breakdown of the numbers
of players and equipment required, and are arranged
within each section according to their level of difficulty,
so you can get the fun underway without delay!

**KEY:**

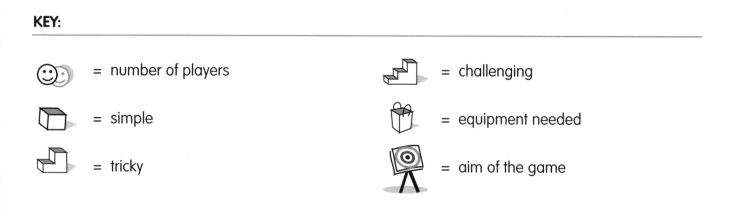

= number of players

= challenging

= simple

= equipment needed

= tricky

= aim of the game

# Indoor Games

# Chain Reaction

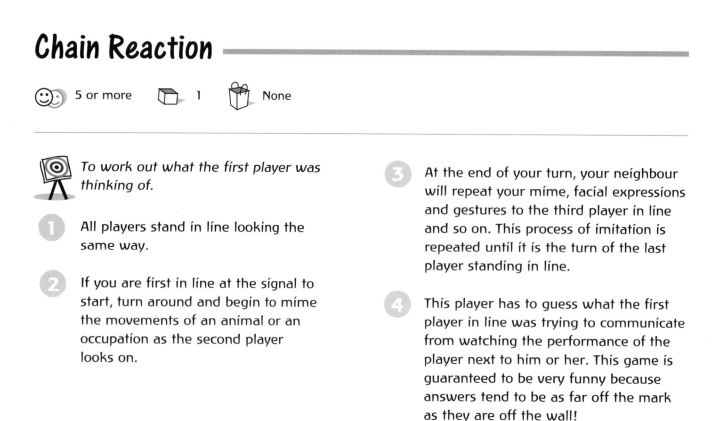

😊 5 or more     📦 1     🎁 None

🎯 *To work out what the first player was thinking of.*

1. All players stand in line looking the same way.

2. If you are first in line at the signal to start, turn around and begin to mime the movements of an animal or an occupation as the second player looks on.

3. At the end of your turn, your neighbour will repeat your mime, facial expressions and gestures to the third player in line and so on. This process of imitation is repeated until it is the turn of the last player standing in line.

4. This player has to guess what the first player in line was trying to communicate from watching the performance of the player next to him or her. This game is guaranteed to be very funny because answers tend to be as far off the mark as they are off the wall!

# Bowling with Marbles

 2 or more     🎲 1     🎁 6 marbles of the same colour (for each player), 1 larger marble as the target, a piece of chalk for marking out the playing field

🎯 *To flick your marbles as close as possible to the target.*

**1** Draw a shooting line with the chalk and decide where to place the larger marble.

**2** Players stand behind this line and take it in turns to shoot all six marbles from here when it is their try, one by one, in the direction of the target marble.

**3** You are allowed to hit other players' marbles as well as the larger target marble.

**4** Count up the final score. A marble that gets close to the target is worth one point. If your other marbles are closer to the target than any or some of your opponents' marbles, you get one point for each of these as well.

**5** The player with the highest score wins.

This miniature version of lawn bowling is good for playing indoors on a rainy day. Just remember to keep your hand steady as you strike.

11

# Hot Hands

😊 2    📦 1    🎁 None

*Your reflexes must be razor sharp. The player with the fastest reflexes (who can pull his or her hands away quickly enough from his or her opponent and avoid being slapped) wins the match.*

**1** Face your opponent. Hold out your hands, palms up. He or she puts his or her hands on top of yours, palms down.

**2** Try to slap his or her hands before he or she can pull them away.

**3** Swap over once you have managed to touch the hands of the other player (even the smallest slap counts!).

**4** Each hand slap is worth one point.

**5** The first player to score three points is the winner.

The game is called hot hands because you have to pretend that your partner's hands are burning like red-hot coals and that you'll get scalded if he or she touches you. You'll both get quite warm from all this hand-slapping as well. Remember not to hit too hard! – you don't want sore hands at the end of the game, do you?

12

# Ball in the Bucket

 1 or more, plus an adult for some assistance  ☐ 1  A bucket, a hoop, some rope or string, a ball, a piece of chalk

 *To get the ball through the hoop and into the bucket beyond in three throws.*

**1** Place the bucket on the floor. Ask an adult to hang the hoop by a piece of string or rope from the ceiling a short distance away from the bucket.

**2** With the chalk, mark out the throwing line on the floor (about 2 metres/ about 6 feet away). You can only throw from behind this line.

**3** You get three attempts to try and throw the ball through the hoop and into the bucket. Good luck, you're dealing with a tough challenge!

**4** You get one point for every successful throw.

**5** If you are not playing alone, the person with the highest number of points at the end wins.

13

## Musical Chairs

8 players, plus a leader

1

A chair for all but one of the participants, CD player, CDs

 *To see who is fastest in sitting down when the music stops.*

**1** Draw lots or flip a coin to choose a leader. This person is in charge of switching the music on and off. He or she is like a referee and watches what is going on to make sure there is no cheating going on.

**2** Before the music comes on, stand around in a circle facing sideways. (Players will not be able to see that there is one chair less than there are players.) For example, if four players are in the game there will only be three chairs up for grabs.

**3** When the music starts, circle around the chairs quickly. At no time can you touch a chair or you will be out.

**4** When the music stops, quickly sit down on one of the chairs. Whoever remains standing on that turn is out.

**5** The winner is the person who manages to sit on the one remaining chair when there are two players left.

# Four Corners

😊 9 or more   📦 1   🎁 None

 *To be the last player to go out.*

**1** Find a large room or garden. Draw lots or flip a coin to decide who is going to be 'it'.

If you are 'it', close your eyes.

**2** The other players break up into small groups. Each group is told to go and stand in one of the four corners of the room (corners 1, 2, 3 and 4) or one of four designated spots in the garden.

**3** Call out a digit from 1–4. Whoever is occupying the corner that corresponds to that number, must sit down. If they do not obey instructions, they are out.

**4** Continue calling out numbers from 1–4 until there are only four players left (one in each corner).

**5** Whoever is last to be out is 'it' the next time around.

# Banana, Knife and Fork

 6 or more    1    2 stools, a pair of washing-up gloves, a large banana, a coin, a napkin, a knife, a fork, a plate

 *To try to eat as much of the banana as you can before the next player lays his or her hands on the napkin, cutlery and gloves and takes your place 'at the table'. If you finish the last slice, you have won!*

1. Place the two stools side by side: the plate and the cutlery go on the first stool; the napkin and gloves on the second.

2. Players sit around the two stools in a circle. The youngest participant is the first to have a go.

3. When it is your turn, spin the coin in front of the other players. If you get 'heads', do not budge. If you get 'tails', rush over to the second stool, tie the napkin around your neck, pull on the gloves and start to slice up the fruit (the only way to eat banana in this game).

4. Remember, you cannot tuck in unless the napkin is tied around your neck and the gloves are on, otherwise you lose your turn.

5. If another player comes up with 'tails', he or she will rush over to you.

6. Players take it in turns to spin the coin as they try to get the person eating the banana off the stool.

7. Hand over the napkin and gloves. Tie the napkin around the neck of the other player. He or she must also pull on the gloves before beginning to eat.

8. As you are out, take up your place in the circle once more.

9. The player who finishes the last banana piece is the winner.

# The Vanishing Picture

 3 or more     2    A large photograph or a photocopied page from a magazine or newspaper, scissors, a large piece of card or paper

*To work out what is in the picture from only seeing small sections of it at a time.*

**1** Choose a picture or a photograph that you like and find interesting or unusual. Select one with quite a lot of detail in it to make the game really exciting to play.

**2** Measure the outer edges of your picture from all sides. Cut out twelve smaller pieces of card to the same size.

**3** Cover up the picture by placing these squares of card, side by side, four to a row. Fold over the edge of each piece so it is easy to pick up.

**4** Show the covered picture to the other players.

**5** Players take it in turns to lift one piece of card at a time so they glimpse only a small portion of the image and never the whole. From this partial information, they must try to guess what is in it.

**6** The first person to guess the picture correctly is the winner.

When your eyes cannot see something as a whole, your imagination will help fill in the blanks!

# Total Recall

 2 or more, an adult to supervise

 2

20 objects (teacup, flashlight, biscuit, lightbulb, spoon, leaf, hairclip, necklace, toothbrush, a set of keys, a coin, paper cup, apple, bracelet, the game rubber band, yo-yo, paperclip, sweets, thimble, tennis ball), a tea towel, paper and pencil for every player

*Use your eyes and photographic memory to recall as many of the objects shown as you can.*

1. Find a table or a flat surface. Ask an adult to prepare a tray with a collection of twelve different objects and then cover the display with a tea towel. The more different these objects are from one another, the more your brain will have some hard remembering to do! Make sure that no one (including you) knows what these items are in advance.

2. Everyone gathers around the covered tray. The supervising adult removes the tea towel for 3 minutes. Use this time to record what items there are and any specific details about the way they look.

3. When the time is up, the tray gets covered up again – no peeking is allowed!

4. Everyone writes down a list of what they have just seen. You get one point for every item remembered correctly and lose a point for mentioning things that were not actually there.

5. If two or more players list the same number of objects and there is a tie, the more precise description wins. For example, it is better to say, 'a yellow tennis ball' than just 'a tennis ball'.

6. The player who remembers the most objects correctly is the winner. If you get really good at this game, you can increase the number of objects that are on display.

# The Waiter

5 to 15          2          Paper and pen

*The player who is the waiter has to remember his 'customers' orders correctly while a lot of commotion goes on in the background.*

**1** Draw lots or flip a coin to choose the waiter.

**2** The other players sit down at a table. While waiting for the waiter to come and take their orders, everyone pretends to begin having a heated discussion with raised voices and lots of hand movements – all of this is of course a distraction tactic.

**3** If you get picked to be the waiter, come over to the table and ask each person for his or her order (including drinks). Listen hard and take in all this information without writing anything down.

**4** You can jot down notes but only once all orders have been placed or afterwards for double-checking answers.

**5** The game can be cranked up a notch by giving the waiter very detailed orders. For example, 'a BLT [bacon, lettuce and tomato] sandwich with fries on the side', 'a slice of cherry pie with lots of whipped cream' or 'a bowl of spaghetti with grated melted cheese on top'.

20

# Human Chairs

😊 6 or more      🪜 3      🛍 None

---

🎯 *To lean back and sit on the knees of the player right behind you to form a human chain. Lean too far back and everyone falls down. It is a real balancing act.*

**1** Stand in line and face in the same direction with your arms wrapped around each others' waists.

**2** Remember: the first player in line is being hugged from behind while the last player in line only does the hugging.

Everyone else in between is being hugged as they do the hugging.

**3** Now it is time for all six players to play the role of a chair. Gently bend your knees forwards before slowly easing back onto the lap of whoever is immediately behind you! If you do not feel very stable in this position, try raising your heels off the floor as this can sometimes restore a little extra balance.

# Tchuka Ruma

 1     3     5 small bowls, 8 pebbles

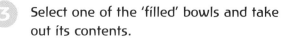

*To collect all your counters in the 'ruma' (the only empty bowl from your original setup).*

**1** Place the five bowls in a row. Starting from the left and moving across to the far right, add two pebbles to each bowl.

**2** Keep the bowl furthest to your right (the 'ruma') empty.

**3** Select one of the 'filled' bowls and take out its contents.

**4** Start to 'sow' the pebbles (one by one) like seeds into the other bowls in a counterclockwise direction. Start from the left and move across to the right to distribute these pieces among the neighbouring bowls.

**5** If your last pebble ends up in the 'ruma' bowl, you can move it from here by selecting the contents of a new bowl. If you have pebbles left over after 'sowing' the 'ruma', carry on distributing these pebbles into any adjacent bowls starting from the left.

**6** If you place your last pebble in a bowl that is full, you must take out all the pebbles and repeat the 'sowing' process described in step three.
If you end up placing the final pebble in an empty bowl that is not the 'ruma', the game is over.

**7** You win when all pebbles are collected in the 'ruma' bowl.

Did you know that Tchuka Ruma is a traditional game of solitaire from Malaysia and the Philippines? It is played on a circular board with a ring of holes on it. One of the holes, the 'ruma' (or home), is larger than the others. At the beginning of the game, all holes, except the 'ruma', are filled with an equal number of stones. The goal of the game is to collect as many stones in this empty hole as possible.

# The Ice-Skating Rink

 2 or more, the help of an adult for hammering in the nails

3

A sturdy board (approx. 1 x 1.5 metres/3 x 5 feet), nails, a hammer, a thick glass bottle, sand, washing-up liquid, pencil

◎ *To complete the racing circuit by sending the bottle skidding between the nail tracks.*

**1** Use a pencil to sketch a racing circuit of two parallel lines (about 25 centimetres or 10 inches apart). The borders of the track must be wide enough for the bottle to fit easily through them.

**2** Ask an adult to hammer in the nails so they follow the shape of the parallel lines you have drawn. Nails should be hammered in halfway through the board with a gap of 3 centimetres (just over an inch) between each one.

**3** When the circuit is ready for racing, add a squirt of washing-up liquid to the surface of the board to help the base of the bottle glide along more easily.

**4** Fill up half the bottle with sand to make it heavier and more stable.

**5** Place the board on the floor and the bottle at the starting line.

**6** Lift one end of the board and begin to gently tilt it this way and that so the bottle swerves as it skates down the circuit. Make sure it does not roll over.

**7** If the bottle falls or rolls over at any time, it is the next player's turn and you have to go back to the beginning.

**8** The player to reach the finishing line first is the winner.

# Outdoor Games

# Red Rover

10 or more (an even number), plus an adult to supervise the game

1

None

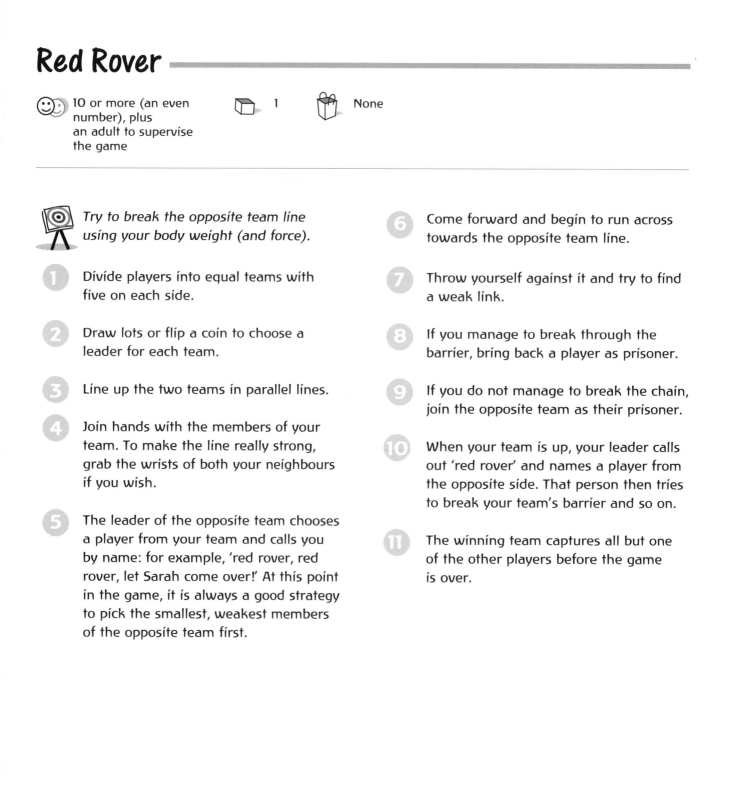

*Try to break the opposite team line using your body weight (and force).*

**1** Divide players into equal teams with five on each side.

**2** Draw lots or flip a coin to choose a leader for each team.

**3** Line up the two teams in parallel lines.

**4** Join hands with the members of your team. To make the line really strong, grab the wrists of both your neighbours if you wish.

**5** The leader of the opposite team chooses a player from your team and calls you by name: for example, 'red rover, red rover, let Sarah come over!' At this point in the game, it is always a good strategy to pick the smallest, weakest members of the opposite team first.

**6** Come forward and begin to run across towards the opposite team line.

**7** Throw yourself against it and try to find a weak link.

**8** If you manage to break through the barrier, bring back a player as prisoner.

**9** If you do not manage to break the chain, join the opposite team as their prisoner.

**10** When your team is up, your leader calls out 'red rover' and names a player from the opposite side. That person then tries to break your team's barrier and so on.

**11** The winning team captures all but one of the other players before the game is over.

This game favours players who are physically strong so, for fair play, participants should be of a similar size, if possible.

# King (or Queen!) of the Hill

 3 or more, plus an adult to supervise the game  ☐ 1  🎁 None

 *To protect your territory from attack and not get knocked off your perch by the other players.*

**1** You can play this game anywhere, on any surface – grass, sand or snow – but find an area where there is a hill, a mound or a high point. Avoid playing in trees and from branches.

**2** This game can get quite rowdy so please do not injure either yourself or your friends by unnecessary pushing and shoving – biting, kicking and any other foul play is strictly not allowed!

**3** Draw lots or flip a coin to see which player gets to be king or queen.

**4** The king or queen climbs the hill to take his or her place at the top of the mound. The king or queen has to beat off any attackers who will clamber up to try to pull, push or shove him or her out of the way.

**5** The attack continues from all sides until the king or queen has been forced off the hill.

**6** The first player to scramble up to the hilltop and claim it is the next king or queen.

If you were a king or queen, you'd defend your kingdom against an invading enemy, wouldn't you?

28

# Red Light, Green Light

😊 4 or more    ▢ 1    Stones, sticks or chalk

🎯 *To tag the player who is the stoplight.*

**1** Draw lots or flip a coin to choose one player to be the stoplight.

**2** If you are the stoplight, stand facing a tree or a wall.

**3** The starting line is marked out on the ground in chalk (about 10 metres or around 30 feet away from you).

**4** The other players line up along this line in a row.

**5** When you call out 'green light!', all the players behind you must move forwards as quickly as possible before you call out 'red light!' and turn around. When you do, everyone must stop where they are. Whoever budges even a little must return to the starting line. The game continues with you calling out another 'green light!' and so on.

**6** The first person to reach you wins and becomes the stoplight in the next round.

This game teaches you the rules of traffic so it's very important to learn it well.

29

# Hunter and Watchman

4 or more    1    None

 *If you are the hunter, to capture as many animals as possible. If you are an animal, not to get caught by the hunter or the watchman and to free as many of the other animals as you can.*

**1** Draw lots or flip a coin to choose two players to be the hunter and the watchman.

**2** The watchman stands in the middle of a circle clearly marked out with a border of stones. He or she cannot leave the circle until the game is over.

**3** If you are an animal, start to run around the play area.

**4** The hunter chases after you, trying to catch and bring back as many animals to the circle as he or she can.

**5** The hunter leads any caught animals back to the watchman.

**6** If you have been caught, you can be saved if one of the other animals who is still free touches you before you are led into the circle. To do this, players must avoid stepping into the circle or touching another player once he or she is within the circle.

**7** If you are tagged by the hunter or the watchman as you are trying to save one of the other animals, you too are now caught and must go into the circle.

**8** The game can be stopped at any moment.

# Capture the Flag

😊 6 or more     ⬜ 1     🎁 2 rags, a piece of chalk for marking out game areas

🎯 To steal the other team's flag without getting tagged.

1. Find a large play area.

2. Divide players into two teams, with an equal number on each side.

3. Draw lots or flip a coin to choose a leader for each team. Hand each leader their team flag.

4. Divide up the playing field so there is a middle area where members of both teams can run around chasing each other and two prisons (at either end) where members of the opposite team are held once they are tagged or captured. Your team's prison area doubles up as your team's safety area.

5. Hide your team's flag. The opposite team does the same.

6. Both teams then break and run across the middle of the playing field trying to steal the opposite team's flag. You must make it back to home base without getting tagged. If you get tagged, you go to the other team's prison.

7. The only way to get out of jail is for one of your team-mates (who is not in prison) to touch you inside the area and free you. Be careful, however, because you can get recaptured if tagged on the opposite side of the field.

8. The first team to find the other group's flag and bring it to their side of the boundary line wins the game.

This game involves a lot of running around so you might be out of breath by the end of it!

# Freeze

4 or more     1     None

*To tag the last player before any other person can crawl between his or her legs and 'unfreeze' them.*

**1** Draw lots or flip a coin to decide who will be 'it'.

**2** If you are 'it', whenever you touch someone that person must remain 'frozen' in place with his or her feet apart. He or she cannot move.

**3** This person can become 'unfrozen' if another player manages to crawl between their legs to 'unfreeze' them before you touch them.

**4** The game continues until you have managed to freeze all the other players.

**5** The last person to be frozen is 'it' in the next round.

# Hopscotch

 6 or more    2    Piece of chalk, counters (stones, bottlecaps, shells or buttons)

To hop through the pattern on one foot without losing your balance.

**1** Use chalk to draw the hopscotch pattern on the ground as shown. Create a pattern with eight squares and number each one. Add a dome-shaped rest area at one end of the pattern where you can pause for a second or two before hopping back through.

**2** Each player selects a counter. Draw lots or flip a coin to decide who goes first.

**3** If you are the first player, stand behind the starting line. Toss your counter in square one. Hop over square one to square two, then continue hopping all the way over to square eight, turn around, and hop back down again. Pause in square two to pick up your counter, hop in square one, and out.

**4** Toss your counter in square two. All your hopping must be done on one foot unless there are two squares side by side. In this case, you can place one foot in each square. Remember to always hop over the square where you have placed your counter.

**5** You are out of the game if you make any of these mistakes: your counter fails to land in the proper square; you step on a line or lose your balance when bending over to pick up your counter and put a second hand or foot down; you hop into the square where your counter lies; you put both your feet down on a single box.

**6** At the end of your turn, place your counter in the square that marks the point from which you intend to continue playing when it's your turn again. It's now the next player's turn, and so on.

This game is sure to keep you on your toes!

# Hole-in-One

2 or more     2     Plastic cup and coin (for each player)

To aim your coin into the cup.

1. You and your opponent can play this game in your driveway or the pavement outside your front door.

2. Lay the plastic cup on its side.

3. Sit or crouch on the ground (2 metres or around 6 feet away from the cup).

4. Take it in turns to aim for the hole (cup) by rolling a coin towards it.

5. Each time the coin rolls in, you have scored a hole-in-one and one point.

6. The player with the highest score wins.

To score, keep your eye on the hole in the ground like a golf pro.

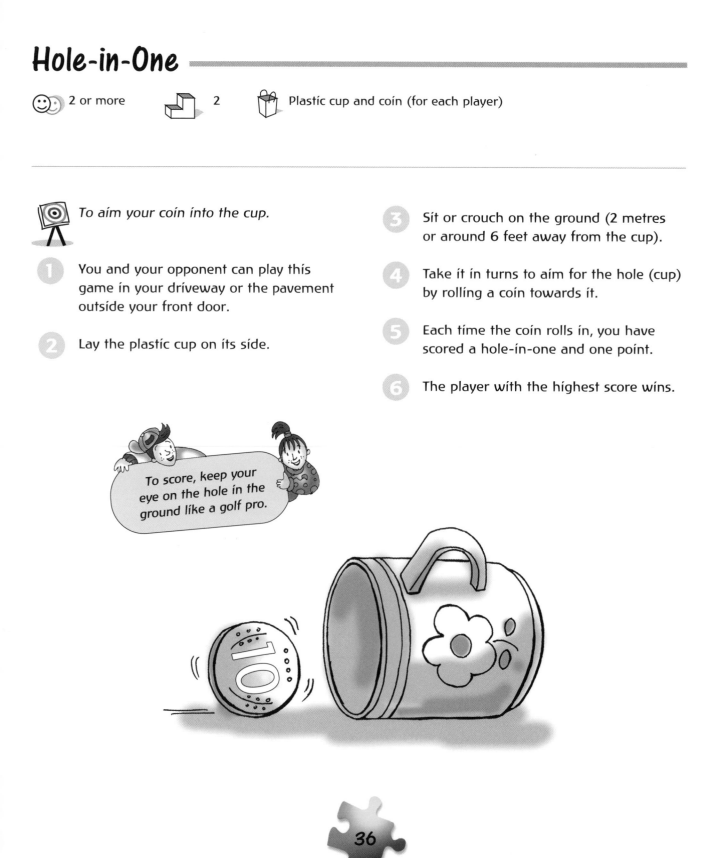

# Beanbag Toss

😊 2 or more    ⬛ 2    🛍 Beanbag, a piece of chalk

 *To hit the marked sections of the target board (especially the bullseye) with your beanbag.*

**1** Use chalk to draw the various sections of your target board. Each section needs to be wide enough so that a tossed beanbag will fit easily without touching the borders. Make sure that the overall structure is roughly round.

**2** Choose a point range from one to eight and mark each section with one point. Make sure that the highest points appear at or near the centre and the lower points further out.

**3** Draw the throwing line (about 1.5 metres or 5 feet away from the target board).

**4** Players take it in turns to toss the beanbag at the target board – make sure you are standing behind the throwing line as you take your aim.

**5** Points are scored if the beanbag falls within a section but you get no points if it just touches one of the borders.

**6** You can win in one of two ways: either by achieving the highest score or by being the first player to reach a maximum set score.

Why not divide your bullseye up into 'slices', like a pie or a dart board, to make it a little different from the norm?

37

# Dodge Ball

10 or more    2    A soft rubber ball, piece of chalk

*To hit as many players from the rival team as you can and dodge their ball to avoid getting tagged.*

1  Agree the size of the play area (10 x 4 metres/33 x 13 feet is a good size).

2  Mark it out in chalk.

3  Divide players into two teams so they face each other across the dividing line.

4  Each team sends one of their members to the opposing team's prison area. These two voluntary prisoners are placed here to get the game started. They will rejoin their team once a member of the opposing side gets hit and takes his or her place in prison.

5  During the game, players must stand within their respective boundaries.

Whoever is in possession of the ball tries to strike someone from the opposite team. If you score a hit, this person is sent to prison behind your team. If you are caught, you have to go to their prison but are allowed one more throw. From prison, you can catch any stray balls or block passes and try to hit rival players. If you do, you earn back your freedom and can return to your team.

6  Remember, the ball can never bounce before it touches a player – if it does, that person is tagged and must go to prison. If someone accidentally catches the ball, whoever threw the ball is out of the game.

7  Continue to play until all players from one team are in prison. The last player to go to prison gets three last ties to try and save himself.

# Tug-of-War

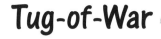 6 or more, plus an adult to supervise the game    3    A rag, a long piece of sturdy rope

 *To pull the opposite team over to your side past the central marker.*

**1** Divide up into two equal teams (in terms of size and strength).

**2** Tie the rag to the middle of the rope as a marker.

**3** You can play this game on a soft surface like grass or sand.

**4** Line up each team, one person behind the other, at either end of the rope. Leave about 1.5 metres (or 5 feet) of clear rope between the two teams.

**5** Pick up the rope. The end player on either side acts as the anchor – it's best to choose the strongest member of your team for this.

**6** When both teams are in position, the supervising adult calls out 'ready, get set, go!' and both sides start to pull in opposite directions. Use all of your strength to try and drag the other team over to your side.

**7** If the first member of the other team crosses the rag, your team wins.

This is a classic contest of strength, coordination and teamwork. You have to work like two opposing forces of nature.

# Mini Olympics

 8 or more    3    A piece of chalk, water, 2 plastic bottles, flour, plastic cups, 2 tennis balls, ruler

 *For your team to score as many points as possible on a flour race, a throwing match and a tickling championship. Let the games begin!*

**1** Players are divided into two teams and set three tasks. At the end of each task, the teams swap over before moving on to the next challenge.

**2** In the first task, members of your team carry handfuls of flour. From the sidelines (marked out in chalk) members of the opposite team are on standby with water-filled plastic cups. They will try to chuck water over you as you race by. Try to reach the finish line without the flour getting wet. If a player from your team does accidentally get theirs wet, he or she must go back to the starting line, to get another handful of flour and restart the race. If he or she can do this within a fixed amount of time your team scores one point.

**3** In the second task, your team is given a plastic bottle filled with water. Set it up some distance away. The opposite team try to knock it over with a tennis ball. Every time there is a hit, a member of your team must run out and set the bottle up again before more water pours out. The opposite team can continue to throw the ball to try and topple your bottle as long as there is water in it. When the bottle is finally empty, the number of direct hits are tallied up and a point allocated to the opposite team for each hit.

**4** In the third task, everyone in your team puts water-filled plastic cups on their heads. You are allowed to hold on to it with one hand. The members of the other team are then allowed to tickle you for a few minutes to get you to spill some of the water. When the time limit is up, any spilled water is collected and measured out with the ruler. The opposite team scores one point for every centimetre/inch of water dropped.

**5** Count up the points across all three tasks and announce the winning team.

40

This game can get messy, but it's great fun!

# Triangular Tug-of-War

3, plus an adult to supervise the game

3

A piece of rope or a clothesline, three handkerchiefs

*To be the first to grab your handkerchief off the ground.*

**1** Contestants should be of similar size and strength. Ask an adult to securely tie a piece of rope (3 metres or about 10 feet long) into a circle.

**2** You and two other players pick up the rope with the same hand. Pull it tight until it forms a triangle. All three of you should be facing outwards so that you are holding the rope behind you with one hand.

**3** The supervising adult places the handkerchiefs on the floor in front of each one of you.

**4** If you are the first player to pick up the handkerchief without letting go of the rope, you are the winner!

This variation on tug-of-war can be played on a much smaller scale either in a confined area or outdoors.

42

# Races and Relays

# Kippers Race

 6 to 20 (divide equally into two teams), plus an adult to supervise the game

1

Card, pencil, crayons, felt-tip pens, scissors, a newspaper or magazine and a paper or plastic plate for each team, whistle (optional)

To land your fish on the plate across the room.

**1** Each player creates his or her own paper fish. Draw the shape out in pencil first. Make sure it measures about 25 centimetres (or 10 inches) from head to tail. Cut your fish out with the scissors and decorate it with crayons or pens.

**2** Line up two or more equal teams of three to five players in a single file at one end of the room.

**3** Place a paper or plastic plate opposite each team at the other end of the room.

**4** When the supervising adult gives you the starting signal or blows a whistle, the first player in each team puts his or her fish down on the floor and begins to race it across the room by fanning it with a newspaper or magazine. Try to create a strong current of air so your fish takes off in the right direction and hopefully lands on or near the plate.

**5** Players from each team take turns flapping their fish onto the plate.

**6** When your fish finally flops onto the plate, race back to your team and give the next player in line the newspaper or magazine so they too now get the chance to fan their fish.

**7** The first team with a plate full of kippers is the winner!

It doesn't matter if you accidentally fan a fish off the plate – what's important is to keep the fish moving...

# Sack Race

 2 or more, plus an adult to supervise

1

Sacks (or sleeping bags or pillowcases) for each player, piece of chalk, whistle (optional)

*To be the first player to hop over the finishing line in a sack.*

1. Find an area with a soft surface like grass or sand. Give each player a sack, sleeping bag or pillowcase and line them up at the starting line.

2. With the piece of chalk, mark out a finish line about 9 metres (or 30 feet) away.

3. When the supervising adult calls out 'on your marks, get set, go!' or signals the start by blowing a whistle, each player climbs into his or her sack. Hold it up around your body and get moving.

4. Whoever is new to this game will do belly flops pretty much immediately because it takes quite some skill to move inside a sack without getting your legs tangled up. The trick is to take long strides as if you were walking. If you do fall over, stay in the sack and pull yourself back up to continue racing.

5. The first person to hop over the finish line is the winner. If teams are competing against each other, the first team to have all its players complete the course in the same sack is the winner.

Be prepared to take a lot of tumbles as you enjoy this very physical challenge!

45

# Racing Bunnies

 8 to 30 (an even number), plus an adult to supervise the game

1

Stones, chalk or sticks for marking outlines, whistle (optional)

*To bounce your way to the finish line.*

1. Using the piece of chalk or the sticks and stones, mark out two lines on the ground (about 5 metres or 16 feet apart). These will be your starting and turning lines.

2. Divide players up into two equal teams with four or more players on each side.

3. Everyone lines up behind the starting line in single file. When everyone is ready, the supervising adult shouts 'on your marks, get set, go!' or signals the start by blowing a whistle.

4. As the first player of your team, you must race towards the turning line madly hopping like a human bunny. To do this, squat your legs and lunge forward. When you get to the turning line, turn around and hop back towards the finish line. Your team-mates can only set off once you (the first bunny) have completed the course and given the second bunny permission to race.

5. The first team to make it out and back are the bunny-hopping champions!

Who will be the happiest, 'hoppiest' bunny around?

# Three-Legged Race

 4 or more
(an even number),
plus an adult to
supervise the game

 2

A large scarf for every pair of players or some short pieces of
rope, chalk for marking out starting and finish lines, whistle
(optional)

 *To be the first three-legged team
(or pair of players) to cross over
the finishing line.*

**1** Find a fairly soft surface on which to
play to avoid injuries. Mark out the
starting and finish lines with the piece
of chalk. They should be about 10–
12 metres (or 33–39 feet) apart.

**2** Divide up into teams that are equal.
Choose your partner and make sure you
are both standing side by side. Bend
down and securely tie his or her left leg
to your right leg with the rope or scarf

(bind together only the inside legs).
Put your arm around your partner's
shoulder. The other pairs of players
do the same.

**3** When everyone is ready, the two
teams line up behind the starting line
in double file.

**4** When the supervising adult calls out 'on
your marks, get set, go!' or signals the
start by blowing a whistle, you and your
partner (as the first couple from your
team) run towards the finishing line. Be
prepared to take a few tumbles as you
find your racing rhythm!

**5** If you and your partner do fall over,
just get straight back up and continue
to race. Turn round at the finish line
and race back to tag the second couple
in your team.

**6** The first team to have its couples
complete the race wins.

In this relay,
choosing a
partner the same
height as you can
really help keep you
steady when you
move together
as one.

47

# Twisted Arms Race

 8 to 20, plus an adult to supervise the game

 2

A pile of about 50 small objects (buttons, bottlecaps, conkers, coins, etc.), whistle (optional)

*To complete a double pass down the team line in the fastest time possible. Use your right hand and pass from the front as you receive an object. Use your left hand and pass from the back as you return an object.*

**1** Divide players into two equal teams. Choose a captain. All players sit down on the grass or the pavement.

**2** Team-mates sit in a line to the left of their leader and the two teams face each other.

**3** Ask a supervising adult to place a pile of objects next to each leader.

**4** When everyone is ready, the supervising adult says 'on your marks, get set, go!' or signals the start by blowing a whistle. Each team captain starts to pass an object from down his or her end of the line, one at a time, to the player sitting down next to them. Objects can only be passed from the front using the right hand.

**5** When an object reaches the opposite end of the line, the last player must now transfer the object to his or her left hand. Objects on their way back to the head of the line (and the captain) can only be passed from the back using the left hand.

**6** The captain begins to make a small pile of returned objects.

**7** Your team leader must be careful not to mix up new and returned objects in the same pile.

**8** Continue passing objects in both directions until all have been returned to your captain.

**9** The fastest team with the least mistakes are declared the winners.

The successful team will be able to work like an automatic conveyor belt!

In this game, you really have to concentrate on what you're doing. It's easy to forget which hand you need to use as you pass or receive the different objects.

# Egg-and-Spoon Race

 2

5 or more, plus an adult to supervise the game

A metal spoon and a hard-boiled egg (for each player), whistle (optional)

 *To race across the room balancing an egg on a spoon without dropping it.*

**1** Players line up against a wall holding a spoon by the handle. In the spoon is an egg. Everyone gets a little time to practice balancing their egg on their spoon before the race starts.

**2** Ask an adult to place a chair about 2 metres (or just over 6 feet) away from the wall on the other side of the room.

**3** When the supervising adult shouts the word 'go' or signals the start by blowing a whistle, players race across the room, trying to keep the eggs balanced on their spoons. If your egg falls off, you cannot continue the race until it's back on the spoon. If it breaks, you're out of the game. Hopefully, there won't be any mess on the floor!

**4** The first person to reach the chair, go around it from behind and cross the finish line with their egg intact on their spoon is the winner. If teams are competing against each other, the first team to have all its players complete the course is the winner.

It's a good idea to have water and a towel handy to clean up any mishaps. Be prepared to make a little bit of a mess so remember to wear old clothes! Don't forget to ask an adult for permission if you're playing the game indoors.

Races and relays don't necessarily have to be competitive with a winning and a losing team. Sometimes it's fun to just play and encourage everyone to take part.

# Wheelbarrow Race

4 or more (an even number), plus an adult to supervise the game

 3

stones or sticks for marking out lines, whistle (optional)

 *To finish the race as a pair with one of you supporting the other by the legs as he or she crawls forward using only the arms.*

1  On grass or soft sand, use a stone or a stick to mark out both the starting and finish lines (10 metres or about 30 feet apart from each other).

2  Divide everyone up into pairs and choose your partner.

3  Pairs of players line up along the starting line as they prepare to get into the human wheelbarrow position. One player from each pair gets down on their hands and knees.

4  When the supervising adult calls out 'on your marks, get set, go!' or signals the start by blowing a whistle, pick up your partner's legs. Hold them by the ankles at waist height as you try to 'push' your partner (the human wheelbarrow) towards the finishing line.

5  Remember, broken wheelbarrows must be picked up where they collapsed – they cannot walk to the finish line!

6  The first pair to cross the finish line or the first team to have all its pairs complete the course is the winner.

You and your friends will end up with really mucky hands in this classic picnic race! Don't forget to scrub up with soap and water afterwards!

# Leapfrog Race

😊 6 or more (an even number) plus an adult to supervise the game

3

Stones or sticks for marking out lines, whistle (optional)

◎ *To hop over any players (or team members) who are crouching down in a flying race to the finish.*

1 On grass or soft sand (to avoid injuries), use a stone or a stick to mark out the starting and finish lines (anywhere between 15–30 metres or about 50–100 feet apart).

2 Divide up players into two equal teams.

3 As the first player from your team, you must crouch down, palms flat on the ground, chin tucked into your chest. This is a little like curling yourself up into a human ball.

4 The other players line up behind you.

5 When everyone is ready, the supervising adult shouts 'on your marks, get set, go!' or signals the start by blowing a whistle.

6 The second player runs up behind you, places his or her hands on your back and vaults over you with his or her legs spread wide apart.

7 After clearing you, it is now their turn to squat down as a third teammate leaps over both of you and so on.

8 The first team to leap their way over to the finish line is the winner.

This bouncy game is an absolute classic – feel the adrenaline rush as you clear the heads of the other players!

# Piggyback Race

 4 or more (even number), plus an adult to supervise the game

3

Stones or sticks for marking outlines, whistle (optional)

 *To carry your partner on your back, swap over, then race back to the finish line as a pair.*

**1** Find a spot where there is grass or soft sand to avoid any injuries. Using a stone or a stick, mark out the start and turning lines (they should be 10 metres or about 30 feet apart).

**2** For a proper race, divide everyone into pairs or teams of at least three pairs.

**3** Line the players up in position along the starting line.

**4** When the supervising adult calls out 'on your marks, get set, go!' or signals the start by blowing a whistle, climb up onto your partner's back and loosely wrap your arms around his or her shoulders. Leave your legs dangling by their waist.

**5** Your partner holds onto your legs and carries you piggyback as you both head towards the turning line. When he or she sets you down, you swap over. This time, you are the carrier and your partner the 'piggy'!

**6** Race back to the starting line as a pair. If teams are playing, the second pair runs the course after the first pair have come back and so on.

**7** The first pair or first team to cross the finish line are champions.

Children under the age of seven should not carry their friends piggyback as they have not yet got the strength or balance to! Older children may carry younger ones though.

# Crab Relay

 8 to 30 (an even number), plus an adult to supervise the game

3

Stones, chalk or sticks for marking outlines, whistle (optional)

---

*To crawl to the finish line making crab-like movements.*

**1** Using the piece of chalk or the sticks and stones, mark out two lines on the ground (4–6 metres or about 13–19 feet apart). These will be your starting and turning lines.

**2** Divide players up into two equal teams with four or more players on each side.

**3** When everyone is ready, the supervising adult shouts 'on your marks, get set, go!' or signals the start by blowing a whistle.

**4** As the first player of your team, you must scurry sideways towards the turning line (like a crab) and then come back to the starting line.

**5** The second player from your team can set off once you have returned and so on. The other players follow your example.

**6** The winning crab crawlers are the team who first complete the race.

Picture how crabs scurry along the beach and you're halfway there!

# Pass-the-Orange Race

8 or more (an even number), plus an adult to supervise the game

3

2 firm oranges, whistle (optional)

 *Players must pass the fruit to their team-mates using only either their feet or chin. Avoid dropping the orange on the ground or using your hands.*

**1** Divide players into two equal teams. Choose a captain for each side.

**2** Everyone takes off their shoes and sits down on the floor in a line facing the opposite team.

**3** The players' legs must be close together, side by side and facing forward, with pointed toes.

**4** When the supervising adult calls out 'ready, get set, go' or signals the start by blowing a whistle, the first player (or captain) is given an orange to place on top of his or her feet.

**5** The object of the game is to move the orange down the line to the next teammate who in turn balances the piece of fruit on his or her feet and moves it on. If you drop the orange before it reaches the feet of the next player, pick it up (using only your feet) and try to pass it on.

**6** The first team to successfully pass the orange down their line are champions.

**7** In a variation of the game, players stand side by side in line and pass the orange by tucking it under their chin and nuzzling it under the chin of the next player. The choice is yours!

How do you prefer to pass the orange? Using only your feet or tucking it under your chin and nuzzling it over to the next player?

# Hunts and
# Hide-and-Seeks

# Ghost in the Graveyard

3 or more     1     None

*For the ghost to tag as many players as he or she can.*

1. Find a big playing area at dusk with specific landmarks like a tree, fountain, porch or a shed. These will serve as safe bases for players running away from the 'ghost'.

2. Choose a player to be the ghost or 'it'. The roles here are the opposite of those in *Classic Hide-and-Seek* overleaf. In this game, 'it' hides while the other players stay at the base and count backwards from 50 to 0.

3. When the counting is over, players move away from the base looking for the missing ghost.

4. If you are picked to be the ghost or 'it', do not wait to be found. Run around creeping up on the other players and try to tag as many of them by surprise as you can before they make it back to the base.

5. If the roles are reversed, for example, and *you* spot the ghost coming, warn the other players.

6. Tagged players are out until the end of the round when there is no one left to tag or players have safely reached the base.

7. At the end of every round, those players who are still safe count backwards again.

8. Players who have already been tagged become ghosts, and team up with you (if you are the ghost) to chase down the remaining players until there is only one person left.

9. The last player 'alive' wins.

This classic run-and-chase game contains elements of tag and hide-and-seek so parts of it may sound very familiar to you.

# Classic Hide-and-Seek

😊 3 or more    🎲 1    🛍 None

 *To find and tag as many players as possible before they reach home base.*

1. Agree on the boundaries of the hiding area and the location of the home base (this could be a step, patio or porch) with the other players.

2. Draw lots or flip a coin to decide who will be the seeker or 'it'. This person will have to search for all the other participants once they have gone into hiding.

3. If you are 'it', close your eyes and slowly count to 50 or 100 while the remaining players rush to find good hiding places.

4. When you have finished counting, call out 'ready or not, here I come', and set out to look for the hidden players.

Players can come out of hiding and run for the safety of home base when you are looking in the wrong direction or are momentarily distracted.

5. If you stick so close to the home base that no other player is able to make it back without you tagging them, a 'zone' can be set around it where no player is allowed to hide. In this way, you will be forced to hunt further out.

6. Any players you find or tag are out of the game until the next round when a new 'it' has been chosen.

7. Continue the game until everyone is either caught or home free. The first person you tagged is 'it' in the next round.

 Champion hide-and-seek players are good at choosing their cover and timing their escape, and are full of surprises when they are 'it'!

# Sardines

 3 or more     1     None

*To find the person who is hiding and hide with them.*

**1** All players (except one) close their eyes. This person runs and hides while the others count to 50.

**2** You need a house large enough to have plenty of good places to hide in (for example, behind a door or a curtain, under the bed, inside the shower cubicle, inside a cupboard and so on).

**3** When the counting is over, a second player goes in search of the first who is now hiding away somewhere in the house. If he or she finds the original player, he or she can join this person in their hiding place. If not, that particular seeker is out of the game.

**4** The game continues until all players have had the chance to seek.

**5** Those players still hiding away, packed into small spaces like sardines, are the winners.

This wriggly game lets you join your mates in small, tight spaces where there isn't much room to move around. Try not to give yourself away by laughing!

# Cops and Robbers

 6 or more (even number)    1    None, coin (optional)

 *If you are a cop, to catch as many criminals as you can. If you are a robber, to avoid getting stopped by the long arm of the law!*

1. Divide players into two equal teams. Flip a coin or draw lots to decide who wants to play the cops in the first round.

2. Select a team base that doubles up as a 'jail'. This could be a porch, a patio or a stoop.

3. The cops gather around the home base and count to 50 while the robbers go and hide.

4. When the counting is finished, the cops begin to chase and tag any robbers they touch.

5. Criminals who are caught are automatically led back to jail. A jail-break can be staged by a member of the robbers team if he or she can tag the jail and free all the prisoners inside without being tagged by a cop.

6. The freed prisoners sit out the rest of the game until all the robbers at large have been stopped by the police.

7. At the end of the first round, count up the number of robbers remaining in jail. Are there many prisoners (because there was no successful jail-break) or just one or two?

8. Teams swap over and the new cops round up the new robbers. At the end of the second round, count up the number of prisoners in jail.

9. The team who catches the largest number of criminals when it is their turn to play the cops wins the game.

*Good guys and bad guys battle it out in this classic, action-packed, hide-seek-and-chase game.*

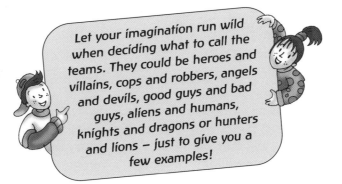

Let your imagination run wild when deciding what to call the teams. They could be heroes and villains, cops and robbers, angels and devils, good guys and bad guys, aliens and humans, knights and dragons or hunters and lions – just to give you a few examples!

# Mice and Wolves

 15 or more, plus an adult or older child to supervise the game

2

Paper, pencils, felt-tip pens, sticky tape

*Depending on which drawing is pinned to your back, your task is to avoid being 'eaten' by those animals who can hunt you and tag the ones who fear you.*

**1** The supervising adult divides players up into five teams – mice, cats, dogs, wolves and hunters – and prepares different animal head drawings for each of the teams. Each player is taken to one side and a piece of paper with a drawing is taped to their back before the game kicks off.

**2** To have a good game, group size should be organized so you begin with the largest group and end with the smallest so, the order should be: mice, cats, dogs, wolves and finally only one or two hunters (no more).

**3** Players spread out across the whole play area and try to go and hide. If you bump into another player, quickly check to see who you are up against. Depending on the animal or animals, you will either run away or give chase. Be prepared for a lightning-fast game as the roles suddenly change and the hunter becomes the hunted (or the other way around).

**4** There are rules to follow: mice can be hunted by everyone except the hunters. Cats can be hunted by dogs and wolves but not by hunters. Dogs chase mice and cats but need to avoid wolves. The wolf can track everyone down but flees from the hunter. If two wolves join forces, they can hunt a hunter.

**5** When someone touches you, you both must go to the supervising adult. He or

A run-or-chase game full of twists and turns, where players either flee from one another or start to run after each other in hot pursuit!

she will place the weaker animal into the stronger group. So, for example, if someone has tagged you (and they are a cat and you are a mouse), you automatically become a cat. This is a general rule of thumb for all animals except two: any animals tagged by the hunter and any hunters touched by two wolves turn into mice.

6 For a fair game at all times, ask the supervisor to keep numbers between animal populations as well-balanced as possible.

7 The game wraps up when the time limit runs out.

# The Great Duel

 8 or more, plus an adult or older child to supervise the game

2

Clothes-peg, piece of chalk, handkerchief (for each player), whistle (optional)

*To collect as many weapons as possible from the rival team.*

**1** Find and mark out a very large play area like the park or the woods.

**2** Divide the players into two teams and give each participant three weapons: a clothes-peg, a stick of chalk and a handkerchief.

**3** At the signal to start, players scatter around this area. When you come across a player from the opposite team, you both must cry out 'challenge!' If you beat your opponent to the battle cry, you decide on which weapon to use for the following duel.

**4** If you choose the chalk, the winner must be first to scribble on their opponent's shoe. If you succeed, the other player must hand over his or her piece of chalk.

**5** If you choose the clothes-peg, the winner must be first to pin it to their opponent's clothes. If you succeed, the other player must hand over his or her clothes-peg.

6. If you choose the handkerchief, both of you must tuck yours into your trouser back pocket so it hangs from behind like a tail. If you succeed in snatching your opponent's handkerchief, he or she must hand it over to you.

7. If one player challenges another with a weapon that he or she has lost, there is no duel.

8. You're out of the game if you lose any of your weapons.

9. After a time, players gather round and the supervising adult starts to stack up the three objects (chalk, pegs and handkerchiefs) to count up how many of each weapon were piled up by each team.

10. The team with the largest number of stolen weapons wins.

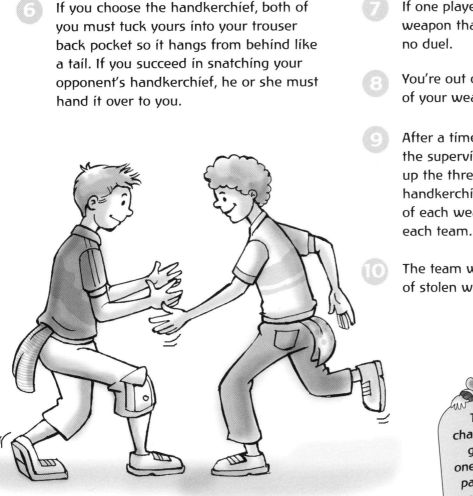

This large-scale chasing game is three games rolled into one – tag, a version of paper/scissors/stone and hide-and-seek – and it'll really put you through your paces!

67

# Key Hunt

😊 8 or more    2    Key

 *If you are the player in the middle of the circle, you need to work out who is holding the key. If you are one of the players sat around the circle, you must try to trick the eyes of the seeker.*

1. All players (except one) sit around in a small, tight circle. Flip a coin or draw lots to see who will be the seeker or hunter of the key.

2. If you are picked to be the seeker, you must sit in the middle of the circle.

3. Close your eyes and slowly begin to count from 1 to 10 as the other players begin to pass the key around in a circle.

4. At the count of 10, open your eyes and try to figure out who is holding the key.

(Meanwhile the key is still being passed from player to player.)

5. You are allowed to watch the other players' movements before making a guess. Remember, to make the fake group passes look realistic, players will be *pretending* to pass the key to each other when actually only *one* person is actually carrying out the action for real.

6. When you are ready, call out the name of your suspect. He or she must open out his or her hand for all to see. If this person is holding the key, you win. If not, you are wrong and must start counting to 10 again with eyes closed.

7. The hunter/seeker has only three tries before he or she loses the game.

The group needs to work very closely together to try and deceive the seeker of the key. Players can even fake or mimic passes to each other but your movements must look realistic and not exaggerated.

# Treasure Hunt

 4 or more, plus an adult to supervise the game

 3

 Pencil and paper, tape, a prize such as sweets or a small toy

 *To follow a set of clues and beat your opponents (or the opposing team) to the hidden prize.*

1. This game is just as entertaining played indoors as outdoors. If you're playing it indoors, find a large room. If not, find a large play area outdoors.

2. Ask an adult to set up the game by hiding away the treasure. A series of written notes must be left scattered around the area of the hunt. These can be taped underneath, inside or behind objects such as furniture, a door, a tree, and so on.

3. Each clue that you find is in some way connected to the next clue – like a chain of information – and the last clue will lead you directly to the treasure. In a well-planned hunt, clues should lead smoothly from one spot to the next and the 'X' that marks the location of the treasure should be chosen so that players don't stumble across it by mistake when following or searching for other clues.

4. The best bit of the game (apart from finding the treasure) are the clues themselves. Clues can be adjusted to the level of the people taking part – obvious and simple instructions for younger children ('Take three steps forward, two steps to the side and turn around') or rhyming riddles and head-scratching puzzles for older children to work out ('I'm full of air but I can't fly' for a bicycle pump, for example).

5. The hunt continues until one player (or team) finds the treasure.

6. The longer the search, the more you'll delight in uncovering treasure at the end!

A treasure hunt can be organized so that players either help each other on their way to the reward or are pitted against one another in their quest for the hidden bounty.

## Scavenger Hunt

 2 or more, plus an adult to supervise the game

3

A piece of paper and a plastic or paper sack for each player; a pencil; timer; a collection of small items (a piece of gum, keyring, photograph, spinning top, toothbrush) as objects to hide around the house

*Players race against each other to hunt down all of the objects on the list within a set time limit.*

1. This version of the hunt is designed to be played indoors by single players.

2. Ask an adult to prepare a list of items that can be easily found around the house.

3. These things should be everyday objects (see below). For younger kids, the list can be very specific while for older players clues can be more open to interpretation. For example, the list could say: 'Find something that goes inside your mouth'. This could be a toothbrush, a toothpick or dental floss, for instance.

4. At the signal, everyone is given a copy of the list and a bag for collecting any objects found.

5. Players set off around the house in search of booty.

6. The first player able to cross everything (or most items) off the list within the time limit is the winner. To make the game more competitive, this hunt can also be played in teams.

Players can get very wrapped up in this game right to the end as they continue to tick items off the list.

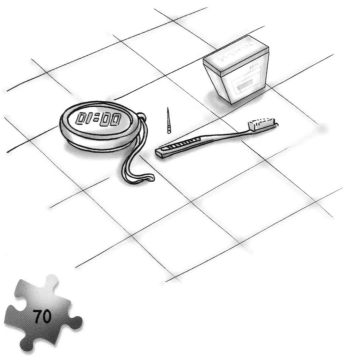

70

# Party Games

## Statues

4 or more, plus an adult to supervise the game          1          None

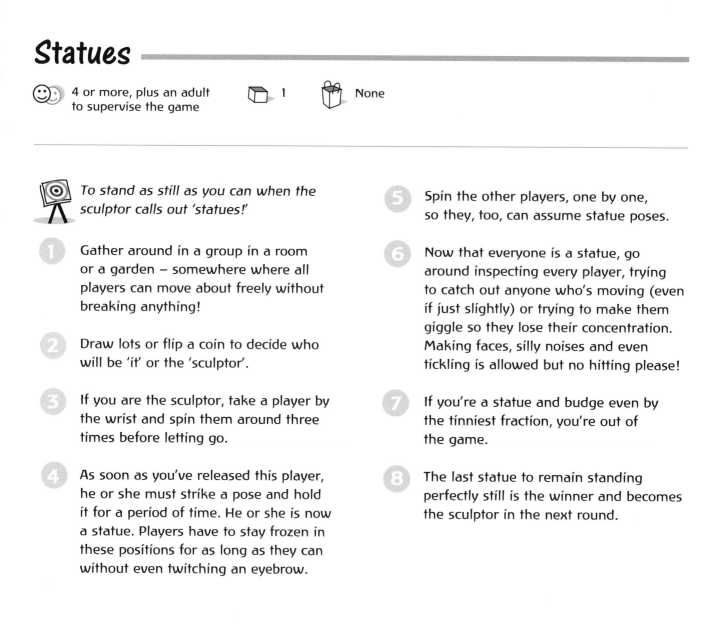

*To stand as still as you can when the sculptor calls out 'statues!'*

**1** Gather around in a group in a room or a garden – somewhere where all players can move about freely without breaking anything!

**2** Draw lots or flip a coin to decide who will be 'it' or the 'sculptor'.

**3** If you are the sculptor, take a player by the wrist and spin them around three times before letting go.

**4** As soon as you've released this player, he or she must strike a pose and hold it for a period of time. He or she is now a statue. Players have to stay frozen in these positions for as long as they can without even twitching an eyebrow.

**5** Spin the other players, one by one, so they, too, can assume statue poses.

**6** Now that everyone is a statue, go around inspecting every player, trying to catch out anyone who's moving (even if just slightly) or trying to make them giggle so they lose their concentration. Making faces, silly noises and even tickling is allowed but no hitting please!

**7** If you're a statue and budge even by the tinniest fraction, you're out of the game.

**8** The last statue to remain standing perfectly still is the winner and becomes the sculptor in the next round.

# The Gods

😊 3 or more, plus an adult to be the DJ

⬜ 1

🛍️ A hardback book for each player, a CD player or radio

 *To move from one end of the room to the other in time to the music (as it switches on and off) without dropping the book on your head.*

**1** Find a space either indoors or outdoors with plenty of room to move around in. Players take all their cues from the music so you have to listen very carefully. Ask an adult or older child to operate the music, switching it on and off as often as the game requires. This game is like a more relaxed version of *Musical Chairs* (see page 14).

**2** Hand each player a hardback book of similar size and weight. If someone is a little older or a little stronger, he or she should be given a book that is slightly heavier than that of the others.

**3** Players spread out around the room. Place the book on your head. Remember, you can extend your arms for added balance.

**4** When the music starts (slow and soft is best), this is your signal to begin walking around the room, stepping forward slowly and gently so the book does not topple from your head. Continue to move so long as there's music playing in the background.

**5** When the music comes to a stop, all players must come to a standstill and slowly go down on one knee. Hold this position until the music restarts, then slowly come back up again and carry on gliding forward. (This is harder than it sounds and concentration is a must!)

**6** If the book happens to slide off your head, you're out of the game, regardless of whether you were walking or kneeling at the time.

**7** The player who can keep the book on his or her head the longest is the book-balancing champion. Congratulations!

*Stand tall and hold your head up high as if you were a Greek god or goddess.*

# Pass the Parcel

 4 or more, plus an adult or older child to be the starter and parcel-wrapper

1

A small toy or sweets, wrapping paper, scissors, tape, a music source that can be easily switched on and off

*To be the first player to unwrap the last layer of the gift when the music stops.*

1. Ask an adult to prepare a mystery present wrapped up in at least ten layers of wrapping paper. The brighter the colours and the crazier the designs of the papers the better!

2. The players sit around in a circle on the floor.

3. An adult or older child switches the music on and players begin to pass the parcel in a clockwise direction.

4. Continue to move the present along from hand to hand until the music suddenly stops. If you are left holding the parcel, unwrap one of the layers and discard the extra paper.

5. The music comes on again and the passing restarts. It is important to keep a cool head in this game as the layers come off one by one as the music stops and starts – it can get nerve-wracking!

6. The player lucky enough to tear off the final bit of wrapping when the music stops keeps the prize.

Be the first person to put their hands on the last layer of the parcel – that way, you keep the surprise that's inside!

# Hot Potato

6 or more, plus an adult or older child if you're playing the musical version

1

Tennis ball or beanbag, which will be your 'hot potato'

*Players must continue to pass the 'hot potato' to each other for as long as they can before the leader calls out 'hot!'*

**1** Find a spot indoors where everyone can sit around in a circle and somewhere where there is nothing to break. Make sure everyone is comfortably sitting down on cushions.

**2** One player sits in the middle of the circle with eyes closed. He or she tosses the 'potato' to one of the other players.

**3** If you catch the potato, you must immediately throw it to another player and get rid of it as soon as you can. The catcher must then do the same and the game begins to really pick up speed.

**4** When the player in the middle calls out 'hot!' all movement stops at once. Be prepared for a sudden change out of the blue – you don't want to get caught with the potato in your hands. Even if the potato is still travelling through the air when someone calls out 'hot!', the last person who touched it gets up and leaves the circle. He or she is out of the game.

**5** Toss the potato back to the starter player who closes his or her eyes and starts a new round.

**6** If the potato is dropped, the player close to it picks it up and puts it back into play.

**7** The game ends with all players eliminated, except one. This player is the winner.

**8** You can also play a musical variation of this game. The potato-tossing begins when the music stops, and ends when the music comes back on again. If you're left holding the potato when the music comes back on, you're out. Sorry!

## Shaving Balloons

 1 or more, plus an adult to check the safety razor covers are on

📦 1

Balloons, string, shaving foam, and a safety razor with its cover firmly on and chair for each player

🎯 *To 'shave' all the foam off a balloon without making it burst!*

**1** Ask an adult to tie up a fully blown balloon covered in foam to the back of a chair with string.

**2** Sit facing the foam-covered balloon with the safety razor in your hand and start to 'shave' off the foam.

**3** You win if you manage to get off all the foam without making the balloon burst.

**4** This game can also be played in teams.

# Pillow Fight

 2      ☐ 1      A long, sturdy wooden plank, 2 bricks, 2 pillows (one for each player), heavy-duty masking tape

As you are both hitting each other with pillows, try to not fall off the plank before your opponent does.

1. Ask an adult to help you create a raised platform by placing one brick under the wooden plank at either end. Masking tape needs to be wrapped around the edges several times to make the structure sturdy and safe for play.

2. You and your opponent step onto the opposite ends of the platform. Holding a pillow in one hand, you advance towards the other player.

3. Hit your opponent with the pillow as you try to keep your balance and wrestle him or her off. Remember, if you don't topple him or her, he or she will topple you instead.

4. You are out of the game if you lose your footing or come off the plank.

Small movements will help you keep your balance better than big, exaggerated ones. Less is more here!

## The Silent Orchestra

 5 or more    2    None

 *To copy what the conductor is doing and silently play (or stop playing) the correct instrument at the right moment.*

**2** Everyone chooses an imaginary instrument to play (including the conductor). Violin, flute, piano and saxophone are all good choices.

**1** Draw lots or flip a coin to choose the conductor. He or she leads the game. The rest of the group sits around this person in a circle.

**3** If you are the conductor, lead the way and begin to play your chosen instrument (for example, the flute). Your orchestra should follow your example, pretending to toot, strum and beat their chosen musical instruments.

4. Once all the other players have begun making 'music', switch from your original instrument to one belonging to one of the other players.

5. All members of the orchestra (except for the player whose instrument it is) start to copy the conductor's body movements.

6. The person whose instrument is being mimed, must stop playing at once and cover his or her ears. For example, if you switch from piano to saxophone, the saxophone player must cover her ears while the other musicians play her instrument.

7. When you (as the conductor) switch back to your instrument, everyone else must do the same, including the saxophonist.

8. A player is out of the game when he or she fails to stop and cover his or her ears when it is their instrument that has been selected by the conductor.

9. The last remaining player in the silent orchestra wins and gets to be the conductor in the next round.

As a member of the silent orchestra, you can play any musical notes you want but you must be quiet as a mouse.

81

# Blowing Bubbles

4 or more (an even number)

 2

A washing-up liquid bottle or bubble solution, a bubble wand (for each player), a piece of chalk

 *To blow a bubble and work together as a team to move it across the field past the opposite team's goal line.*

**1** Set up the play area. Mark three parallel lines 2.5 metres (or 8 feet) long with a space of about 95 centimetres (or 37 inches) between each line.

**2** Give each player a bottle of bubble solution and a wand.

**3** Divide the players into two teams. They line up facing each other on either side of the middle line. The goal line is the line behind each team.

**4** The game starts with one player from each team blowing a bubble. As the bubbles rise, the two teams take turns to blow furiously on theirs to send it across the middle line and over the heads of the opposite team into their territory. Your aim is to get your team's bubble past the opposite goal line.

**5** You cannot touch the bubble with any part of your body (including your nose or forehead) but, other than that, anything goes! Do make sure, however, that your bubble does not burst before it's made its way across the field!

**6** Players can cross the central line and chase the opposite team's bubble to move it away from their own goal line.

**7** Your team gets one point if it manages to move the bubble over the goal line of the other team.

**8** If the bubble pops before a goal is scored, the two teams reassemble and start a new round. Teams take it in turns to blow the bubbles.

**9** The team with the most points wins the match.

# Pin the Tail on the Donkey

 4 or more, plus adults to set up the game and spin the blindfolded players

2

A large sheet of cardboard, a paper tail for each player, tape or thumbtacks, paint, felt-tip pens, blindfold, scissors

---

 *To correctly pin the tail on the donkey while blindfolded.*

1. Choose a playing area with plenty of room to move around in.

2. Ask an adult to help you draw a large picture of a donkey on the sheet of cardboard. Hang it up on a wall at eye level.

3. Cut out as many donkey tail strips as there are players. Insert a pin or a thumbtack near one end of each tail otherwise they won't stay on (or use tape instead).

4. Each player writes his or her initials on the tail they are given.

5. Remember, the donkey needs to be facing you from the side. If you want to use other animals, like a lion or an elephant, these, too, will work well with this game.

6. Each player is blindfolded, one at a time, and spun around three times (make sure you don't get dizzy and fall over!) and pointed in the direction of the drawing.

7. Come forward towards the wall and stick the tail as close to the place where a real donkey's tail would be as you can.

8. The player who comes closest to pinning the tail in the right place on the donkey is the winner.

Try to use your memory to picture the donkey in your head!

# Piñata

4 or more, plus an adult to set up the game and spin

 2

2 brown paper bags, newspaper, string, felt-tip pens, tissue paper, tape, scissors, sweets, a stick, blindfold the blindfolded players

 *To strike the dangling piñata and break it open so its surprises come pouring out.*

**1** Ask an adult to make a piñata beforehand (from the items listed above), filling it with sweets and stuffing any leftover space with crumpled sheets of newspaper. Decorate the piñata with the felt-tips and tissue-paper streamers. To do this, cut the tissue paper into strips and stick them on with tape.

**2** Hang the piñata either from a hook in the ceiling (if you're playing indoors) or from a tree branch (if you're playing outdoors), but not too high as you'll need to be able to hit it with your stick.

**3** Players line up and wait their turn. Each one is blindfolded, given a stick and spun around three times.

**4** When it's your turn, swing your stick and try not to miss the piñata. If you do, the next player gets a try and so on until the lucky winner gives it a resounding whack and all the sweets come down like a rainbow!

**5** Everyone scrambles to the floor to pick up as many sweets as their hands and pockets can hold. This game is really lovely because everyone's a winner. The person who bursts the piñata can also be given a special prize.

Aim high but don't whack yourself on the head by mistake! The other players should keep their distance from whoever is holding the stick, too!

A piñata is a container made of paper or newspaper stuffed with goodies like sweets and small toys. The original piñatas were made from simple clay pots or earthenware jars that were filled with trinkets, coins and sweets.

86

# Flicking Balloons

2 or more, plus an adult to start the game

2

An air-filled balloon (for each player), felt-tip pens, whistle (optional)

 *To make your balloon travel the furthest distance across a room using only hand movements to guide it along.*

**1** Remember to play this fun party game indoors because if you play it outdoors your balloons might float away, up into the sky, spoiling all the fun!

**2** Blow up as many balloons with air as there are players. Give everyone a different coloured balloon. If there are not enough colours to go round, players can mark their balloons with a felt-tip pen so there is no confusion.

**3** Line up on one side of the room.

**4** Balance your balloon on the open palm of your hand.

**5** When you hear the whistle, start flicking the balloon off your hand using the thumb and index finger from your other hand.

**6** You can only skim the surface of the balloon – you must never try to pat it, prod it or (worse) push it along. That's cheating!

**7** If your balloon falls to the ground or suddenly bursts, you are out of the game.

**8** The player whose balloon travels the furthest is the winner.

Use controlled flicks of your hand to keep your balloon up in the air for as long as possible.

# Simon Says

 3 or more    3    None

*To copy the actions of the player who is Simon without messing up! He or she, in turn, must say 'Simon says...' every time an instruction is given to the other players.*

1. Draw lots or flip a coin to choose a player to be Simon.

2. The other players stand in a line facing this person.

3. If you are Simon, at the signal to start give the group instructions they can follow. Remember to *always* start any command with the words 'Simon says...' For example, 'Simon says, clap your hands!' or 'Simon says, jump up and down!' Everyone copies your movements and tries not to make any mistakes until you give players a new set of instructions. (Players need to watch out for a fast-talking Simon: this kind of player can really steer the game to his or her advantage!)

4. To clinch the game, players must try to avoid being caught out as you watch their every move like a hawk. Remember, players don't *have* to follow a command unless you say 'Simon says' first. This is the bit of the game that confuses a lot of people and, if you are a quick-thinking Simon, you will use this trick to get players out.

5. Players drop out one by one until there is one person left in the game.

6. This person is Simon in the next round.

Did you know that this game began as an army drill?

# Limbo Dancing

😊😊 4 or more     ▨ 3     📦 A broom handle or a curtain rail

*To clear the stick or rail from underneath by twisting or bending backwards but without losing your balance or touching it with any part of your body.*

**1** Two players hold up the stick at chest height at either end.

**2** The other players line up in single file and try to shimmy under the stick but without touching it at any time.

**3** Shuffle your feet forwards as you try to shimmy backwards with your arms held out for balance. Your head must be the last part of your body to go under the stick. It can be quite tricky!

**4** When everyone's had their turn, lower the stick a notch so the twisting can start all over again but with gradually less room to move around in. Going under the stick without making body contact becomes more and more difficult.

**5** You're out if you bump your head, lose your balance or touch the stick. See if you can hold out the longest!

**6** The last player to be out is the champion limbo dancer.

**7** You can also play this game to music (which might help you to coordinate your body movements better).

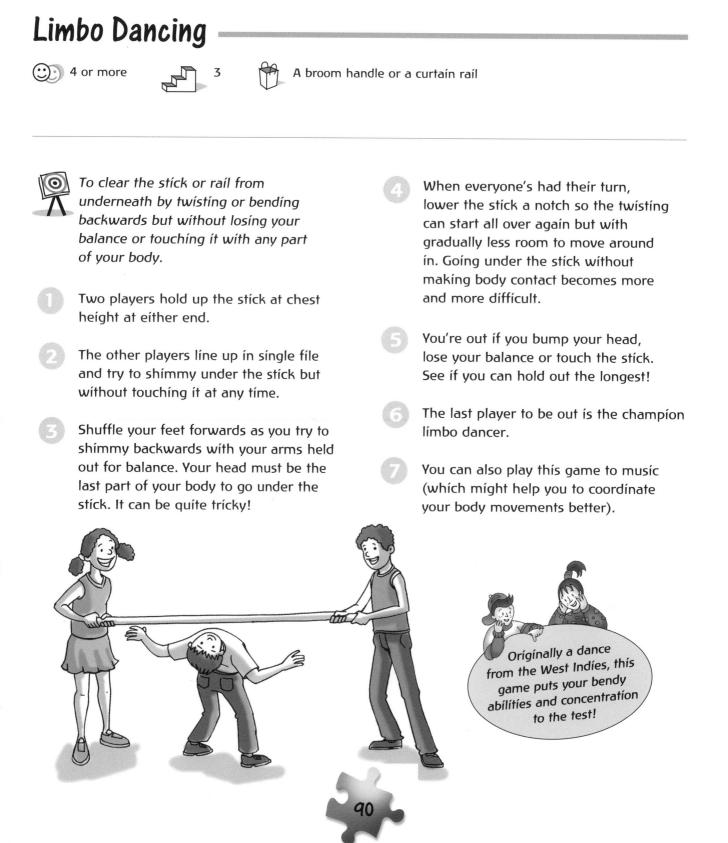

*Originally a dance from the West Indies, this game puts your bendy abilities and concentration to the test!*

# Guessing Games

# I Spy

😊 2 or more     ⬜ 1     🎁 None

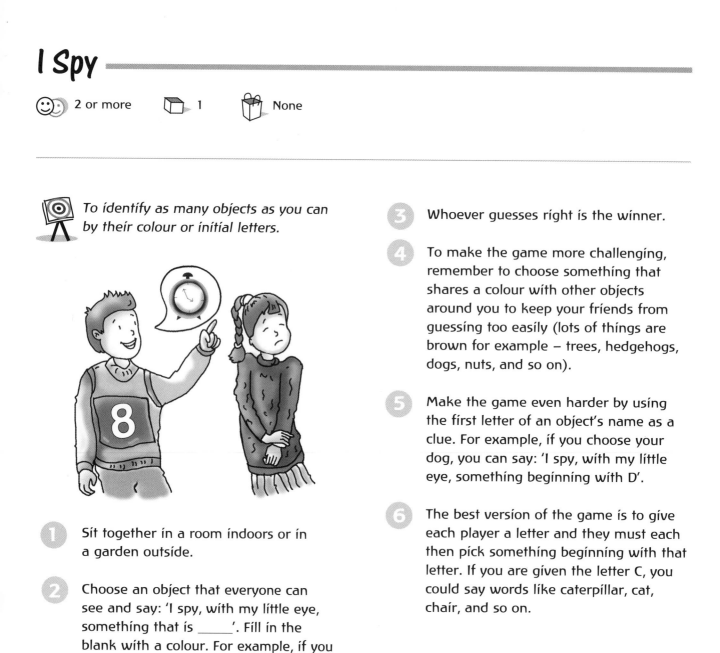

🎯 To identify as many objects as you can by their colour or initial letters.

**1** Sit together in a room indoors or in a garden outside.

**2** Choose an object that everyone can see and say: 'I spy, with my little eye, something that is _____'. Fill in the blank with a colour. For example, if you were looking at a clock, you would say: 'I spy, with my little eye, something with HANDS'.

**3** Whoever guesses right is the winner.

**4** To make the game more challenging, remember to choose something that shares a colour with other objects around you to keep your friends from guessing too easily (lots of things are brown for example – trees, hedgehogs, dogs, nuts, and so on).

**5** Make the game even harder by using the first letter of an object's name as a clue. For example, if you choose your dog, you can say: 'I spy, with my little eye, something beginning with D'.

**6** The best version of the game is to give each player a letter and they must each then pick something beginning with that letter. If you are given the letter C, you could say words like caterpillar, cat, chair, and so on.

This game can be a fun way of practicing the letters of the alphabet.

# What Am I Tasting?

😊 2 to 15      📦 1      🎁 Different types of food, bowls, teaspoons

🎯 *To guess the name of the food you are being given to 'eat' without peeking through the blindfold. Let your tongue (not your brain) do the guesswork here!*

**1** Prepare several bowls, each containing a different kind of food (for example, jelly, mustard, ketchup, baby food, flour, jam, peanut butter). Put a teaspoon in every bowl.

**2** Blindfold the tasters.

**3** Each taster then tries a spoonful of the contents of each bowl.

**4** Tasters can identify which foods they are trying by taste alone. Deciding on whether a mystery substance tastes salty, bitter, sweet or sour can sometimes tell you what you have in front of you.

**5** Whoever gets the most correct guesses wins.

**6** You can also play this game in teams.

Did you know that certain parts of your tongue (known as the taste buds) are more sensitive to specific flavours such as sweet, salty and sour? Your tongue is like a food map and it may not like everything that it tastes!

# What Am I Touching?

 2 to 15      1      Objects different in texture (wet sand, chestnuts, semolina, ice cubes, fruits and vegetables, jelly, etc.)

*To guess the objects you are given to touch.*

**1** Choose a group of objects from around the house that are different shapes and sizes. Make sure they feel quite different from one another – some can be smooth, others rough; some cold, others warm, and so on.

**2** Players take it in turns to be blindfolded. When it's your turn, you must guess the object's or substance's identity only through touch. Players can also put their hands behind their back when being handed objects. Good luck – see how many you get right!

**3** Whoever gets the most correct guesses wins.

**4** You can also play this game in teams.

# What Am I Smelling?

 2 to 15  1  Strong-smelling items (coffee, fresh herbs, spices, mint leaves, etc.), dark plastic containers with lids, a blindfold

*To recognize a wide variety of smells.*

1. Ask an adult to help you find several strong-smelling items. For example, lemon, orange peel, cedar wood, perfume, pine needles, coffee, vanilla, onion, mint, vinegar, moth balls, sawdust, ginger, peppermint and pencil shavings are all good choices.

2. Place each one in a different container and cover with a lid so the odours don't mix.

3. Players take it in turns to be blindfolded. When it's your turn, you must correctly identify a broad range of smells. Don't worry, your nose won't let you down. What memories do you recall with particular smells?

4. Whoever gets the most correct guesses wins.

5. You can also play this game in teams.

Did you know that your brain helps you to recognize a smell?

# Pictionary

😊 4 or more    2    A sheet of paper and a pencil

 *One player does a drawing of a word picked by the opposite team. His or her team-mates have to guess the word within a given time limit.*

**1** Divide the players into two teams, with the same number of players on each side.

**2** Draw lots or flip a coin to see who goes first.

**3** The team who wins chooses a word for the other team to guess.

**4** The team who loses picks one of its players to be the artist.

**5** As the artist, you're responsible for making a sketch of the word suggested by the opposite team. Your team-mates will have to guess the word and you cannot give them *any* clues.

**6** Someone from the first team comes over and whispers the word in your ear.

**7** Once you've understood what the word is, start to draw the object. During this time, you cannot talk, gesture or make noises. Your team-mates, however, can say as many words out loud and make as much noise as they want.

**8** If your team guesses the word correctly before the time runs out, they score one point. (A team has one minute to try to come up with the correct answer.) You and your team choose a word for the opposing team to guess the next time.

**9** If your team guesses the word incorrectly or after the minute is up, the first team wins and they get to choose another word to be drawn.

Ready? Set? Draw! You do not need to be an artist to excel at this great draw-and-guess game, where the originality of what you sketch is half the fun (and often gives away good clues, too).

# Rhyming Charades

 4 or more       2       Pencil and paper for keeping score

 *Having been given a rhyming word as a clue, discover the mystery word by using pantomime to check your guesses with the audience.*

1. Divide players into two teams. Team one is the actors and team two is the audience.

2. Team one leaves the room while team two decides on the word to be acted out by team one.

3. Once this is chosen, team two chooses a word that rhymes with the mystery word. This word must be given to team one as a clue.

4. The more rhymes the mystery word has the better.

5. Team two returns to the room and is given the rhyming word as a clue.

6. It must now use pantomime to check their guesses with the audience. For example, if the mystery word is 'took', players may want to act out 'cook' or 'hook' in front of the audience by pretending to whisk eggs or go fishing. If the acting is good, the audience will call out 'No, it's not cook!' or 'No, it's not a hook!', and so on.

7. Actors are allowed up to three guesses. If team one guesses correctly before all three attempts are up, the point goes to them. After that, the point is awarded to the audience team for having stumped the team of actors.

8. Teams swap over at the end of the first round. The new audience team chooses a word.

9. Teams swap over yet again at the end of the second round.

10. Teams carry on alternating roles until one team scores 10 points and is declared the winner.

# Who Am I?

😊 4 or more     ⬛ 2     🛍 Headbands, sticky labels, felt-tip pens

 *To guess the name of the person written on your headband.*

**1** Players sit around in a circle and are given headbands to tie around their heads.

**2** Every player also receives a blank, sticky label. Write down the name of a famous person on the label and stick it on the headband of the player opposite you.

Be careful no one sees you writing this name down because that would give the game away!

**3** When everyone else has finished doing the same and is ready to play, players start to ask each other questions about the name on their foreheads.

**4** The first player to figure out who they are is the winner.

# What's that Tune?

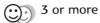

😊 3 or more      📶 3      🎁 None

 *To guess the name of a tune after hearing only a few notes.*

**1** Choose a player to be the hummer or singer. If you are this person, start the game by humming or whistling the first note of a well-known pop song.

**2** The other players try to guess the name of the song from that single note. Players take it in turns trying to guess

the famous melody. You'll see how just tricky it is to do!

**3** Now repeat the beginning of the melody, adding one note each time until someone finally guesses the name of the song.

**4** This person becomes the singer in the next round.

*Music fans with a good ear will relish this memorable musical guessing game.*

# Murder in the Dark

 10 or more     3     Playing cards

 *A killer is hiding among the players! The detective must unmask him or her by staging an interrogation and asking questions.*

**1** Gather all the players in a room, preferably one lit by a single light switch.

**2** Take out the same number of cards from the deck as there are players. Make sure you include the king of diamonds and jack of spades.

**3** Each player selects a card and looks at it before discreetly putting it away in his or her pocket. Whoever chooses the king of diamonds is the detective. Whoever chooses the jack of spades is the killer.

**4** The light is switched off and players start to move about in the shadows.

**5** If you are the detective, stand by the light switch, ready to turn it back on.

**6** In the dark, whoever is the killer chooses his or her victim by putting both hands on this player's shoulders. This person lets out a scream and falls down to the ground. Don't be frightened – no one gets really hurt as it is all pretend!

**7** After 10 seconds, switch the light back on.

**8** This is your chance to take action: take out your card as ID and start an interrogation among the other players. It's best to question them as a group rather than one by one. Ask lots of questions about their whereabouts and alibis (like where they were last, where they have been since, who they were with, etc.).

**9** As the detective, you have four chances to discover the identity of the killer. If all four guesses are wrong, you are out of the game. If you unmask your villain, you can consider yourself the pride of the police department!

**10** Players who are wrongly accused can show their cards to prove their innocence.

# Charades

😊 6 or more     3     Pencils, scraps of paper, a bowl

*You need to work out the title, word or phrase that another player is trying to mime or act out according to a set of pantomime rules.*

1. Each player is given several scraps of paper on which to write down words or phrases that fall into a single category or a group categories (for example, titles of books, television shows, movies or proverbs). If you are playing more than one category, each player must write down their name and the category of the word or phrase they have chosen.

2. These pieces of paper are folded up (to hide the answers) and mixed up in a bowl. These are the charades. Players take turns dipping into the bowl for charades.

3. Dip your hand into the bowl and pick up a charade. Read its contents to yourself and think how you are going to mime it in front of the other players. Read out the name at the bottom of the scrap of paper. This person sits out the round.

4. Players have a time limit of 3–5 minutes in which to guess your charade. As you start and continue your mime, give the other players a series of clues about the nature of your charade using only these standard hand gestures and body language. Here's a guide:

* **A book title:** put your hands together as if you are praying then unfold them flat like the pages of a book.

* **A film title:** form an 'O' with one hand to imitate a camera lens while pretending to turn the crank on an old-fashioned movie camera with the other.

* **A television show:** make a box with your fingers.

This classic guessing game requires a healthy dose of imagination and works well with mixed-age groups. As you mime, you cannot speak so you must let your hands and body do the talking!

* **A famous proverb or saying:** make quotation marks in the air with your fingers.

* **A famous person or celebrity:** pose with a hand on your chest and the tips of your fingers lightly tucked into your shirt (like Napoleon Bonaparte).

* Pull on your ear to indicate that the word being guessed sounds like another word.

* Hold up your fingers to indicate the number of words in the title, quotation or name.

* Hold up the same number of fingers once again to indicate the position of the word in a phrase the other players have to guess.

* Hold your fingers against your arm to indicate the number of syllables in a word.

* Hold your thumb and forefinger close together to indicate a short word or open them wider to indicate a long word.

* Wipe your hand across your forehead when players' answers are getting 'warm' (their guess is close to the correct answer).

* Cross your arms and shiver when players' answers are getting 'cold' (nowhere near the correct answer).

**5** The other players continue calling out guesses until the time is up. Confirm any correct answers (or parts of answers) by tapping your index finger on the tip of your nose and point to the person or persons who made the guesses. Shake your head and finger at any incorrect guesses.

**6** Next, it's time for another player to pick up a charade from the bowl and start a new mime.

**7** The player with the highest number of correct guesses at the end of the game is charades champion.

# Hand Games

# Origami Challenge

 1     1     Paper, pencil or pen, scissors and colour crayons

 To make a fully working 3-D object from a flat sheet of paper!

**1** To make a triangle from a rectangular sheet of paper, make a diagonal fold from the bottom-left corner.

**2** Using the scissors, cut off the rectangle at the top.

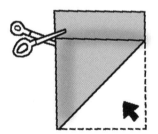

**3** Fold over the two opposite ends of the triangle to form a smaller triangle.

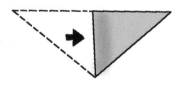

**4** Open up the paper, uncreasing all the folds.

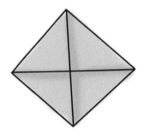

**5** Fold one corner into the centre. Repeat with the opposite corner.

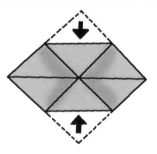

**6** Repeat with the other two corners so you end up with a square.

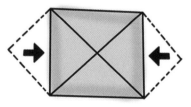

Origami (pronounced or-i-ga-me) is the Japanese art of paperfolding. 'Ori' is the Japanese word for folding and 'gami' is the Japanese word for paper. That is how origami got its name!

**7** Flip the paper over. Fold a corner over the centre. Repeat with the opposite corner.

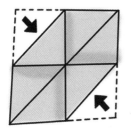

**8** Fold over the two last corners so you end up with a smaller square.

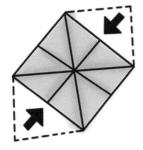

**9** Fold the square in half. Unfold and fold in half the other way.

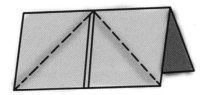

**10** Unfold and pull the four ends together, making a diamond-like shape. Shade each of the square flaps a different colour with the crayons. Pick up each of the flaps and put your fingers inside. Move the four parts around.

This type of mental activity encourages you to 'see' the shape in your head before you fold over the flat surface of the paper and turn it into a three-dimensional object. This skill takes a bit of practice but is very useful for other games as well.

# Paper, Scissors, Stone

 2 or more    1    None

*To defeat your opponent's weapon of choice using one of three hand gestures (paper, scissors or stone).*

**1** Stand or sit facing your opponent with one hand behind your back.

**2** Count 1, 2, 3, then thrust your hidden hand into the centre and quickly make one of three simple hand signs: a closed fist (rock), a flat, open hand, palm-down, with all the fingers extended (paper) or a hand with forefinger and middle finger extended and separated into a 'v' shape (scissors).

**3** The match is won according to these rules:

* The paper covers the stone (the paper wins).

* The scissors cut the paper (the scissors win).

* The stone smashes or blunts the scissors (the stone wins).

**4** If you both choose the same weapon, it's a tie and you both have another go.

**5** The game is usually played for a best score out of five goes.

# The Well

 5 or more    2    None

To match the nouns called out with the correct hand and body gestures.

**1** Stand around in a circle outdoors or in the garden. Draw lots or flip a coin to choose the leader.

**2** Before you start, you must select objects you want to use in the game and give them each a sign. For example, touching your head or any other part of the body.

**3** All players close their right hand into a loose fist. This is your 'well'. Leave a gap in the middle (so the fingers of other players can fit in here).

**4** The leader starts to call out the names of the different objects and players

acknowledge these objects with their free hand using the chosen signs.

**5** When the leader calls out 'my well', everyone inserts their left forefinger into the gap of their right fist.

**6** When the leader calls out 'my neighbour's well', players put their left and right forefinger into the wells of the players on either side.

**7** Anyone who plays the leader will try to catch you out when delivering his or her instructions so that the movement you make doesn't match what gets called out. You have been warned!

To sharpen your concentration skills and to avoid slipping up, try not to look at the leader but focus on what he or she is saying.

111

# String Challenge 1: The Plate and Bowl

 1      2      1 metre (or just over 3 feet) of nylon elastic string tied at the ends works best but normal string or twine is also fine

 *To pull a single piece of string into various loops that together look like 'bowl on a plate'.*

**1** Slip the length of string in front of the fourth, middle and second finger of each hand. Gently stretch the length of string on either side.

**2** Slip your forefingers through the opposing side of the string. Start with your right hand and repeat with your left.

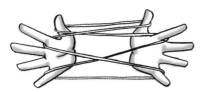

**3** Slip both thumbs under the third loop (start with the loop that is closest to you).

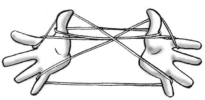

**4** Slide both thumbs under the first loop.

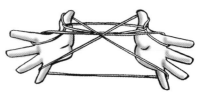

**5** Release the string from your little fingers to achieve the 'bowl-on-a-plate' effect.

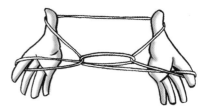

Many shapes and patterns known as figures can be made from a loop of string held between the hands.

# String Challenge 2: The Eiffel Tower

 1    2    1 metre (or just over 3 feet) of nylon elastic string tied at the ends works best but normal string or twine is also fine

*To go from 'a bowl-on-a-plate' shape to the Eiffel Tower in a single move.*

**1** To go from one configuration to the next, catch the uppermost part of the first loop in your mouth.

**2** Release both thumbs and pull down, holding the string firmly through your teeth.

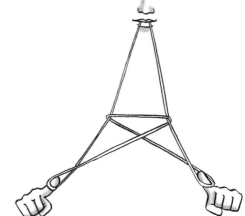

You need nimble fingers to play string games or your figures can literally tie you up in knots!

# String Challenge 3: The Four-Legged Eiffel Tower

 2 (a second player is needed for the final step)

2

1 metre (or just over 3 feet) of nylon elastic string tied at the ends works best but normal string or twine is also fine

 To create a four-legged Eiffel Tower from a single piece of string.

**1** Repeat steps one and two from the Plate and Bowl (see page 112).

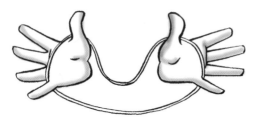

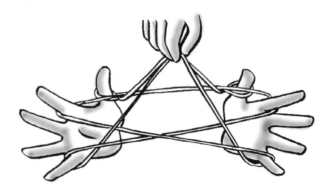

**3** Release the forefingers and pull down to create a four-legged Eiffel Tower from underneath.

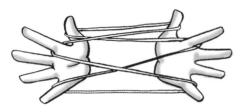

**2** The second player takes his or her hand over the hole in the middle of the configuration to pull up the first and last strings.

# String Challenge 4: The Trapped Hand

 2   3  1 metre (or just over 3 feet) of nylon elastic string tied at the ends works best but normal string or twine is also fine

 *To trap and then free the other player's hand in a few slick moves.*

**1** Repeat steps one and two from the Plate and Bowl (see page 112).

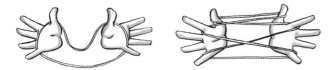

**2** The second player inserts his or her hand through the gap in the middle of the string, then pulls their hand back out again through the space created by his or her thumbs.

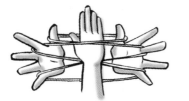

**3** Release your thumbs very suddenly so that the other player's hand stays trapped inside the string.

**4** Repeat steps one and two from the Plate and Bowl (see p. 112).

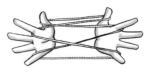

**5** The second player re-inserts his or her hand from underneath through the space in the middle of the string.

**6** Release your little fingers and watch how this move frees the hand of the other player from the string.

String games were traditionally played by the Navajo Indians, the Koreans and the Japanese. It's hardly surprising that string holds such fascination among different peoples as it produces some fantastic results!

# String Challenge 5: Dreamcatcher

 1  3 1 metre (or just over 3 feet) of nylon elastic string tied at the ends works best but normal string or twine is also fine

*To create a woven pattern typical of Native American Indian string art.*

**1** Repeat steps one and two from the Plate and Bowl (see page 112). Release the thumbs.

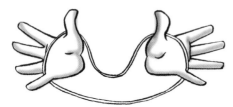

**2** With your thumbs, grab the last strand from underneath and pull it towards you. Your thumbs must both be inside the loop.

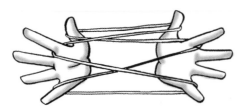

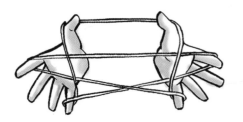

**3** Move your thumbs over the second string to find the third loop. Release your little fingers.

**4** With your little fingers, go over the fourth string and catch the third.

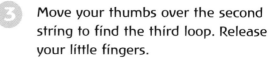

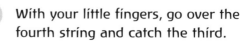

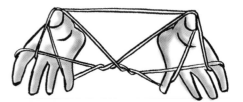

**5** Release your thumbs. Move them over the first two strands so you can trap the third.

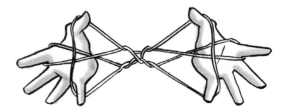

**6** Slide your thumbs inside both forefinger loops.

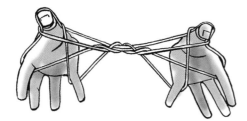

**7** Insert your thumbs between the first and the second strand.

**8** Insert your forefingers inside the first triangular gaps below your thumbs.

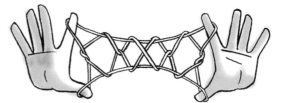

**9** Release your little fingers. With a twisting motion of your hand, you now have a dreamcatcher.

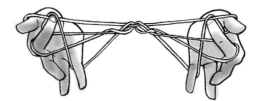

Each string figure has a name. Sometimes songs are sung and stories told as the figures are being made. In Native American Indian culture, dreamcatchers help a person sleep well by warding off bad dreams.

# String Challenge 6: The Parachute, Daddy's Trousers, Mummy's Apron, Granny's Shoes

 1 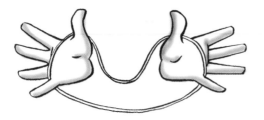 3 1 metre (or just over 3 feet) of nylon elastic string tied at the ends works best but normal string or twine is also fine

*To go from one figure to the next in a series of spectacular string transformations. The other three figures are continuations of The Parachute.*

**1** Repeat steps one and two from the Plate and Bowl on one hand (see page 112).

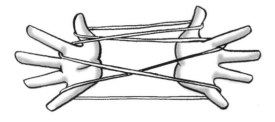

**2** With your other hand, pull the middle string then release it.

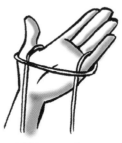

**3** Pull the middle string again.

**4** Move the string to the other side of your hand.

118

**5** With your free hand, pull the thumb and little finger loops.

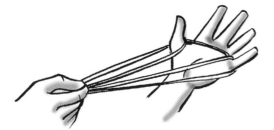

**6** Shift these two loops to the other side of your hand as you place one finger in between each strand.

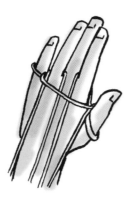

**7** Slide these four strands under the string which is at the top of your hand.

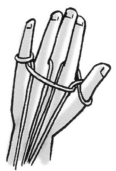

**8** Move the string over to the other side of your hand and pull it towards you. You've just opened your parachute!

These next few figures are quite challenging, so practice hard until they come to you easily. When you've got to grips with it, why not try and tell your friends a story as you're coming in and out of the different figures?

**9** Release the bottom of your parachute. With your other hand, catch the loops behind your forefinger and fourth finger and pull them over these fingers. Pull down.

of daddy's trousers. Pull down. You have just created an apron for mommy!

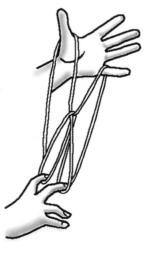

**12** Release your little finger to make slippers for granny!

**10** You've just made trousers with large pockets for daddy!

**11** Release the bottom of daddy's trousers. Place the forefinger and middle finger of your other hand inside the two pockets

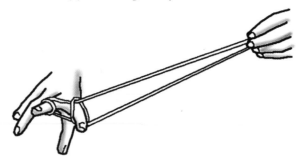

# String Challenge 7: Cat's Cradle, The Manger, Candles and Diamonds

😊 2    🪜 3    🎁 1 metre (or just over 3 feet) of nylon elastic string tied at the ends works best but normal string or twine is also fine

 In cat's cradle, two people make various shapes with a single loop of string, passing it back and forth between their fingers and hands. During this game, you and the other player take turns and remember that instructions often suddenly swap over.

**1** Put your hands through the string. Keep your thumbs out of it.

**2** Loop the string around each hand. Keep your thumbs out of the loop.

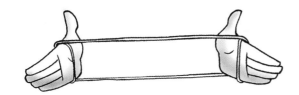

**3** Put the middle finger of your left hand through the loop of your right hand and pull.

**4** Put the middle finger of your right hand through the loop. This is the cat's cradle. The next bit is tricky: find the two places where the string makes an 'X'.

**5** The second player takes his or her thumb and forefinger and pinches the X-shaped parts.

**6** Still pinching the Xs, the second player moves his or her hands further apart until the string is taut.

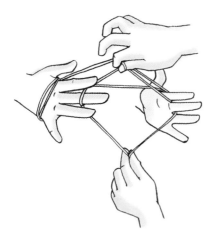

**7** This movement involves pointing the fingers down (through the sides of the string) and then scooping them up through the middle before pulling very gently. While the other player is doing this, do not let the cat's cradle slide out of your hands.

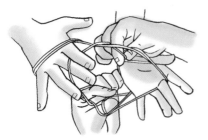

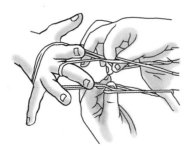

**8** The cat's cradle finally ends up on the second player's hands.

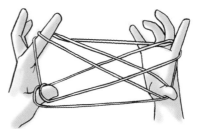

**9** Pinch the Xs from the top, not the sides.

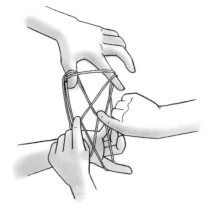

**10** Keep pinching the Xs as you move your hands further apart.

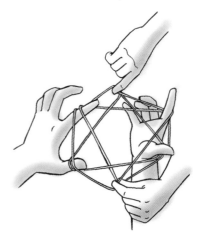

**11** Keeping hold of the Xs, push your fingers towards the middle.

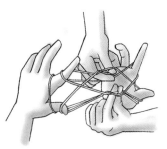

**12** Pull your fingers up through the middle gap in the string and then pull your hands wide apart. You now have candles (or tramlines).

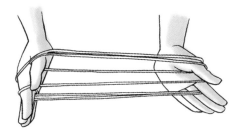

**13** The second player uses the little finger from his or her opposite right hand to pull the left top string far over to the right beyond the outside strings.

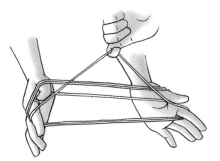

**14** With the little left finger, the second player pulls the right top string to the left so that there are two little triangles.

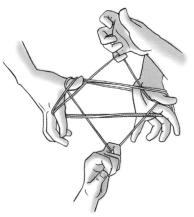

**15** The second player holds the ends of the triangles tightly with the little fingers (that's the hardest part!), turns his or her hands and goes over with the thumb and forefinger. Not for the faint-hearted…

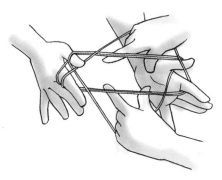

**16** Still holding on tightly with the little fingers, the second player now pushes his or her thumbs and forefingers up through the middle gap in the string.

Cat's cradle is very famous but did you know that there are lots more string figures you can make? For example, the manger, candles and diamonds!

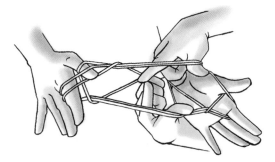

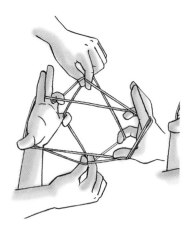

(17) Still holding onto the bottom string tightly with the little fingers, the second player spreads thumbs and index fingers as you let go of the elastic. You're now looking at the manger!

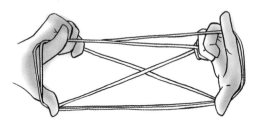

(20) Pull the Xs up a little and, pinching tightly, turn your hands over. Point your thumb and forefinger downwards and dive into the middle gap.

(18) Pinch the Xs with thumb and forefinger.

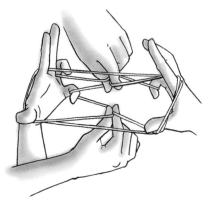

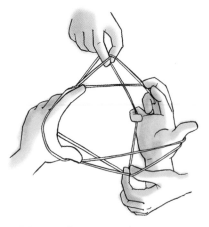

(21) With the fingers still pointing down, spread thumb and forefinger apart to create diamonds.

(19) Still pinching them, pull out the Xs to the sides.

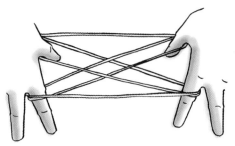

# Paper and Pencil Games

# Little Monster

😊 3          📦 1          🛍️ Paper, pencils and coloured pencils or crayons (optional)

*Players have bundles of fun creating the oddest-looking character by drawing sections of the figure separately without being allowed to see the parts already drawn.*

**1** You will need a rectangular piece of paper (20 centimetres or roughly 8 inches long). Fold it into three sections. Draw two small lines over each crease. The lines over the first fold indicate how wide the character's neck has to be. The lines over the second fold point to the required width of the character's waistline.

**2** Draw a head in the first section of the paper. Make sure your character's neck fits within or is the same thickness as the two markings over the first fold.

**3** Fold your section over so the head is hidden and hand the folded sheet of paper to the second player.

**4** He or she now draws the body in the second section of the piece of paper. The neck line here too should line up with the markings over the first fold. The character's waist must match the gap between the lines over the second fold.

This great game is non-competitive and really creative. It will get your imagination going and let everyone join in (with belly-aching results).

**5** The third player draws the figure from the waistline down to the feet.

**6** Fold out the sheet of paper to view the 'monster' you have created in all its glory. Does anyone around you have a straight face?

# Follow that Line!

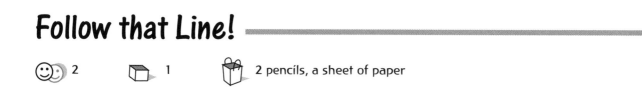

 2       1       2 pencils, a sheet of paper

*To be the first person to cross the finish line.*

**1** Each player is given a pencil.

**2** Copy the racetrack as shown in the diagram. The track should be about a centimetre (or about half an inch) wide. Mark the starting line and the finish line.

**3** Each player takes it in turn to place his or her pencil on the starting line. Hold it in a vertical position with the tip of your finger, then push the pencil down into the paper and gently try to flick it across so it begins to draw a line before bouncing off the surface of the paper.

**4** At the next turn, each player sets out from the point at which the line left the racetrack on the previous go.

**5** The first person to complete the track wins the match.

# OXO

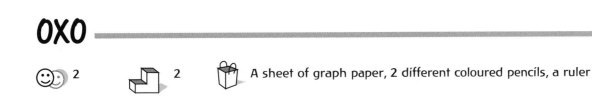

😊 2    ▢ 2    🛍 A sheet of graph paper, 2 different coloured pencils, a ruler

 To spot and strike through as many OXO series inside the grid as possible.

**1** Using the pencil and ruler, draw an 8 x 8 playing grid on graph paper.

**2** Choose who will be Xs and who will be Os. Xs go first. Each player is given a pencil to write down their symbol.

**3** Take it in turns to fill in one square at a time with either an X or an O.

**4** Strike through an OXO sequence – vertically, horizontally or diagonally – on the line intersections and close it off from your opponent.

**5** Every completed series is worth one point.

**6** Whoever has the most points once all the spaces on the grid are full, wins.

This game of tic-tac-toe 'on the lines' can be mastered in a matter of minutes.

# Nim

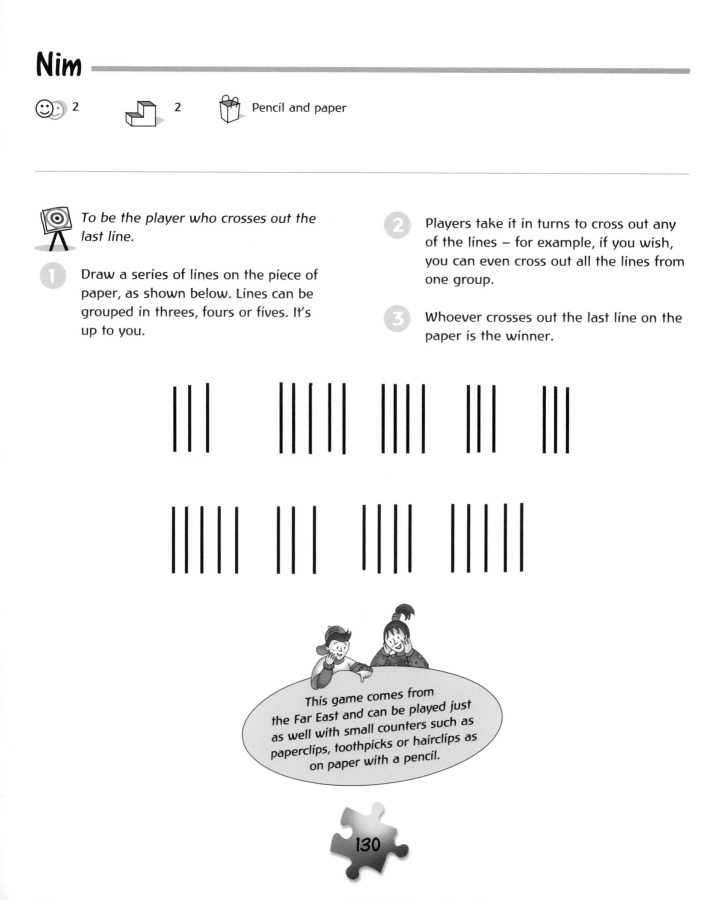

😊 2     2     Pencil and paper

🎯 *To be the player who crosses out the last line.*

**2** Players take it in turns to cross out any of the lines – for example, if you wish, you can even cross out all the lines from one group.

**1** Draw a series of lines on the piece of paper, as shown below. Lines can be grouped in threes, fours or fives. It's up to you.

**3** Whoever crosses out the last line on the paper is the winner.

This game comes from the Far East and can be played just as well with small counters such as paperclips, toothpicks or hairclips as on paper with a pencil.

# Little Squares

😊 2    📦 2    🛍 Graph paper and 2 coloured pencils or felt-tip pens.

 To 'close off' as many of your own squares and prevent your opponent from boxing off as many of his or hers as you can.

1 Draw an 8 x 8 grid on the graph paper – your official play area. Each player is given a pencil.

2 Players take it in turn to mark one side of any square on the grid.

3 If you succeed in 'closing off' a square, put an O or an X in it to claim it as yours. You then get another go. If you manage to 'close off' yet another square, put a mark in it like you did for the first one.

4 Try to mark those places where you can see that your opponent is unable to close off any squares. This becomes almost impossible as the game goes on.

5 When the grid is full, count up both players' squares to find the winner.

An extremely simple game of strategy and a great way to prepare for Battleships (see page 164).

## Tangrams

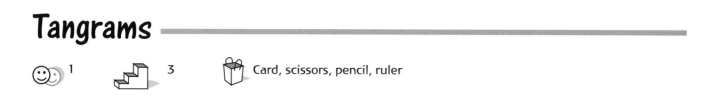

1    3    Card, scissors, pencil, ruler

*To create as many figures as possible from seven tangram pieces cut out from a single piece of card.*

**1** You will need a square piece of card measuring 15 centimetres (about 6 inches) along each side.

**2** Use the ruler and pencil to draw the lines as shown on the diagram. Score the lines with the ruler and cut out these seven shapes using scissors. As you can see, the cuts must be straight lines but they can be made at different angles giving you some quite uneven-looking shapes.

**3** Scramble the pieces. Now start to combine them to create human figures, animals and geometric shapes. The only rule is that you must always use all seven pieces. Below are some examples of the different combinations that you can put together.

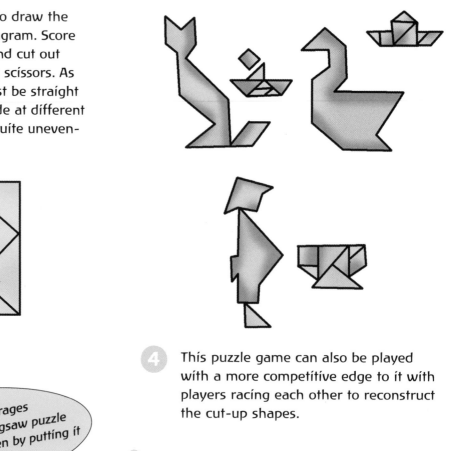

**4** This puzzle game can also be played with a more competitive edge to it with players racing each other to reconstruct the cut-up shapes.

*Playing tangrams encourages you to create your own little jigsaw puzzle – first by taking it apart and then by putting it back together again.*

# Art in the Dark

2 or more, plus an adult as storyteller

3

Pencil, paper and coloured crayons for each player

*To draw a story on paper in a dark room. Results are hilarious!*

1. Find a dark room with a table where all the players can sit down to draw.

2. Give each player a pencil, paper and some coloured crayons.

3. The supervising adult switches off the lights.

4. The storyteller begins his story. For example, 'Once upon a time, there was a mermaid called Heather.' All players are asked to draw Heather. You are given a minute or two to draw this character, then the storyteller continues with the tale.

5. You are given a minute or two in which to draw whatever new part of the story is being added. The storyteller will always pause at this point so players can get on with their drawing.

6. When everyone is finished, the lights are switched back on and the artworks (or better, works of art) are compared for fun.

*You'll get a real kick out of comparing your silly drawings at the end of this game!*

# Tic-Tac-Toe with Numbers

 2     3     Paper and pencil

*To be the first player to complete a line of numbers that add up to 15.*

**1** Draw a standard nine-square grid on the piece of paper with two parallel vertical lines crossed by two parallel horizontal lines.

**2** Your opponent's numbers are the four even numbers between 1 and 9 (2, 4, 6 and 8).

**3** Your numbers are the five odd numbers between 1 and 9 (1, 3, 5, 7 and 9).

**4** You go first because you have one more digit to your name. Write down an odd number in any of the squares on the grid.

**5** Your opponent does the same and writes down an even number.

**6** Race each other to claim any rows of numbers that add up to 15 either in a vertical, horizontal or diagonal line.

**7** The game is won by whoever completes the first line or the most lines.

**8** The game can come to a draw if all of the squares have already been filled.

**9** Swap over being odds and evens for the next round of the game.

This game puts the bite back into the old classic game of noughts and crosses. This version is for older children.

## Growing Crystals

 2 or more        3        A sheet of graph paper, a pencil and a different coloured crayon for each player

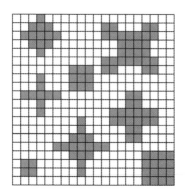

To 'grow' crystal shapes inside the grid by filling in squares and developing symmetrical patterns.

1. Mark off a grid (20 squares by 20 squares) on the sheet of graph paper. If there are more than two players, the grid should be larger (increased by about 10 squares for every additional player).

2. Try to see the shape of your crystal in your head first. It can be a thick or a thin cross, a small or a large square or a diamond-like shape. The crystal shape you decide to fill in must be symmetrical (identical on both sides when an imaginary line is drawn down the middle). Any crystals presented on the grid are only valid if they are symmetrical.

3. You and your opponent take it in turns to colour in the first square of your crystal, one square at a time, bit by bit, as the whole structure grows.

4. At the start of the game, it is probably best to scatter your squares widely across the grid to explore places where you could potentially develop crystals.

5. During the middle and final stages of the game, it is best to focus on smaller areas and concentrate on spreading a single crystal over a wide surface area.

6. Try to obstruct your opponent's crystals before they fully form.

7. The game continues until there are no squares left to fill.

8. Scores are tallied up by adding the number of squares contained within each crystal.

9. The player with the highest number of squares (not crystals) wins the match.

# Word Games

## Antonyms

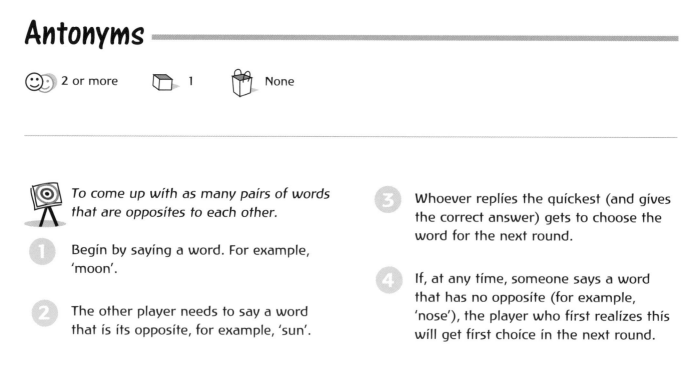

😊 2 or more    🧊 1    🛍 None

🎯 *To come up with as many pairs of words that are opposites to each other.*

**1** Begin by saying a word. For example, 'moon'.

**2** The other player needs to say a word that is its opposite, for example, 'sun'.

**3** Whoever replies the quickest (and gives the correct answer) gets to choose the word for the next round.

**4** If, at any time, someone says a word that has no opposite (for example, 'nose'), the player who first realizes this will get first choice in the next round.

This game requires you to put your thinking cap on and give your partner words that are antonyms (the direct opposite of what he or she has said).

138

# Questions and Answers

3 or more     2     Pencil and paper (for each player)

*To give answers to questions that preferably have no correct answer.*

1. Each player writes down a question on a piece of paper like: 'Why is the earth round?' or 'What came first: the chicken or the egg?'

2. Each player folds up his or her answers so no one else can see them.

3. Collect the sheets of paper. Without unfolding them, mix them up and hand one back to each player. He or she writes down an answer to an invisible question that he or she cannot see.

4. Unfold all the sheets and read out all the answers to the questions, one by one. These are bound to be very illogical so it's going to be mayhem all the way!

# Word Chains

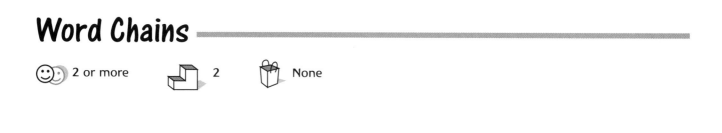

😊 2 or more     🧱 2     🎁 None

 *To repeat the 'chained' word sequence in the correct order.*

**1** Make sure the order of play moves in a clockwise direction so that it's the first player's turn again when the last player has just had a go. It's important that the game proceeds smoothly.

**2** Call out a word – 'house', for example.

**3** The second player repeats 'house' and adds another word (for example, 'plane'). So, the third player needs to say 'house', 'plane' and one other word.

**4** Listen carefully to the words other players are calling out, remember their order and don't forget to tag one more word on the end. Watch as the word chain keeps on growing!

**5** The more times you go around the circle, the more challenging the game becomes and the longer your word list.

**6** If someone gets stumped, the other players can drop hints until no one can remember the chain itself and the game is declared over.

Your brain is given a good verbal workout on this one. Push your memory and concentration abilities as far as you can – it'll pay off!

# The Orchard

 3 or more, a supervising adult to call out different vegetable (or fruit) names    2    None

To correctly call out the manner in which different 'orchard' vegetables (or fruit) grow.

1   Ask an adult to call out the names of vegetables (or fruit), one at a time.

2   Depending on which vegetable (or fruit) is chosen each time, you and other players have to answer whether it grows above ground (for example, tomatoes, lettuce, green beans) or underground (for example, potatoes, carrots, turnips).

3   Whoever gives a wrong reply is immediately out of the game and sits out until the end.

4   On the next round, switch to playing with animal names. Players have to answer 'sky', 'earth' or 'water', depending on where a particular type of animal lives. For a dolphin, for example, you would answer 'water'.

A good knowledge of fruits and vegetables is a real ace up your sleeve here. Now you know why it's important to eat your greens and have your five daily portions of fruit and veg!

# Picture-Word Associations

 3 or more

2

Paper, pencil and a picture or photograph cut out from a newspaper or magazine for each player

 *To look at a picture you have never seen before and guess the same word associations that other players make.*

1. Choose a photograph or an image. Cut it out from a newspaper or magazine without showing it to anyone. Everyone else does the same.

2. Place the piece of paper, pencil and photograph (face down) in front of you on the table.

3. When it's your turn, turn the picture over so it's now face up. Everyone studies the image and are given a minute in which to list any words that spring to mind. For example, a picture of the sun might make you think of how thirsty you get in the heat. You might then think of something thirst-quenching like a cool glass of ice-cream.

4. When the time's up, read out the words you jotted down, one by one.

**5** The other players should shout out if any of their words match yours.

**6** Keep track of the number of identical word picture associations made. Give yourself 1 point for every word match.

**7** Any players who also shared the word association are also awarded 1 point.

**8** When it's the second player's turn, he or she turns over his or her chosen picture, and the game carries on around the table.

**9** Whoever has the highest number of word matches at the end of the rounds, wins.

Are you a mind reader? Play this entertaining picture-word association game and find out!

## Spelling Bee

2 or more, plus an adult to be the 'teacher'

2

A dictionary (optional)

*To spell as many words correctly as possible.*

1. Ask the 'teacher' to prepare a list of words that matches everyone's spelling ability.

2. Players line up opposite each other (if in two teams).

3. The player furthest to your left is given a word to spell which he or she must first repeat, then spell out, then repeat again. For example, 'balloon, B-A-L-L-O-O-N, balloon' etc.

4. If you spelled the word correctly, the next player is given a new word to spell. If not, he or she is given the chance to try the same word that you got wrong, at which point you would be out and have to sit down.

5. The words get gradually harder and harder to spell.

6. Allocate one point for every word that's spelled correctly.

7. The last player (or team-mate) to remain standing wins the contest.

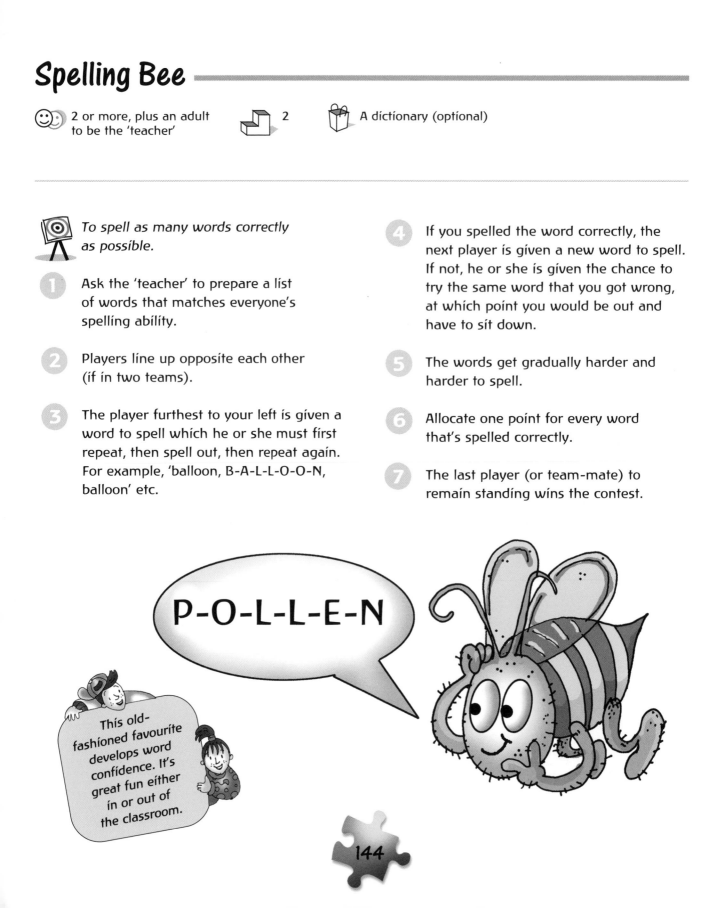

P-O-L-L-E-N

This old-fashioned favourite develops word confidence. It's great fun either in or out of the classroom.

# Earth, Wind, Air and Fire

☺ 6 or more        2        None

To respond with the name of an animal, fish or bird when the correct category is in play.

1. Stand in front of the other players. You can single out anyone at any time.

2. Point to someone and say 'earth', 'air', 'fire' or 'water' and count from 1 to 10 as fast as you can. If you say 'earth', this person must name an animal before you reach 10. If you say 'air', he or she must name a bird. If you call 'water', he or she must name a fish. If you call 'fire', however, players must remain absolutely silent! Also, no two animals, birds or fish can be the same in any one game.

3. You have three tries in total. Each time you mess up, you collect 1 point (for once, not a good thing!).

4. When you reach 3 points, you're out of the game.

5. Continue playing until there is a winner.

A fast-response game where little or no movement is required, but where you need to know when to keep quiet and when to speak out.

145

# Word Factory

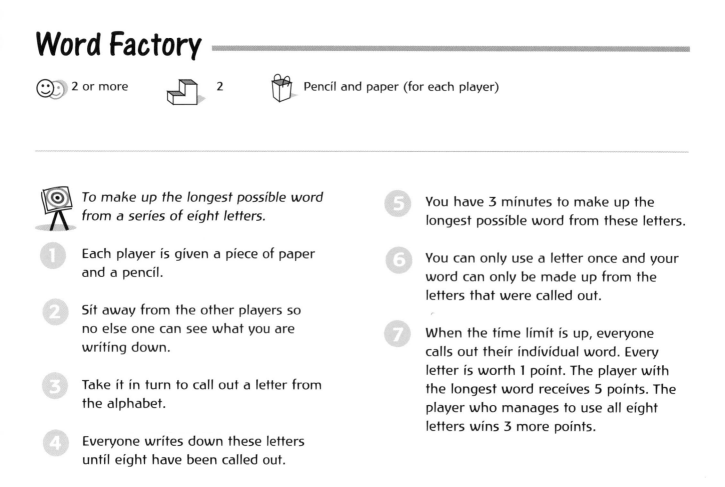

☺ 2 or more        2        Pencil and paper (for each player)

🎯 *To make up the longest possible word from a series of eight letters.*

**1** Each player is given a piece of paper and a pencil.

**2** Sit away from the other players so no else one can see what you are writing down.

**3** Take it in turn to call out a letter from the alphabet.

**4** Everyone writes down these letters until eight have been called out.

**5** You have 3 minutes to make up the longest possible word from these letters.

**6** You can only use a letter once and your word can only be made up from the letters that were called out.

**7** When the time limit is up, everyone calls out their individual word. Every letter is worth 1 point. The player with the longest word receives 5 points. The player who manages to use all eight letters wins 3 more points.

Use a dictionary if there's any doubt about whether the winning word exists or not!

# Hangman

😊 3 or more          2          📦 Pencil and paper

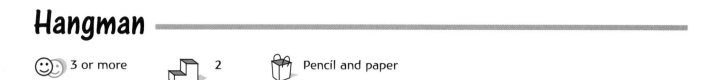

🎯 *To figure out the mystery word, letter by letter, before the hangman gets hung.*

**1** Think of a word and count the number of letters in it.

**2** Draw a line of dashes, one for every letter in your word. For example, the word 'playground' is represented by 10 dashes.

**3** Players take turns calling out letters of the alphabet. Write any correct letters down on the appropriate blank (or blanks if it is repeated). For example, on a word like 'gorilla'.

**4** As the letters get filled in, players may also have a stab at guessing the whole word.

**5** If one of the players guesses a letter that's not part of the mystery word, write it down in a 'scrap heap' on the side of the sheet of paper.

**6** Start to draw the head of the hangman dangling from the gallows above the line of blanks. The gallows can be just an 'L' upside down – they don't have to be anything fancy.

**7** Each incorrect question adds another part to the drawing – a right arm, a left arm and so on.

**8** If players take a lot time to guess the word, they must continue suggesting letters until the hangman is complete – and they have lost.

**9** The player who guesses the word before the figure is complete, wins.

This fill-in-the-blanks game was inspired the television programme, Wheel of Fortune.

# Tongue Twisters

2 or more, plus an adult to provide the twisters

3

A watch or timer

To repeat the given tongue twister out loud correctly.

**1** Ask an adult to help you pick out a well-known tongue twister for you and your friends. Here are some examples:

*She sells seashells by the seashore.*

*Peter Piper picked a peck of pickled peppers.*

*How much wood would a woodchuck chuck if a woodchuck could chuck wood?*

**2** Whoever is able to recite the tongue twister the most times correctly without tripping up or hesitating is the winner.

She sells seashells by the seashore

Peter Piper picked a peck of pickled peppers

This game is real fun to play. You will notice that many tongue twisters have similar letters that crop up again and again. This is known as 'alliteration', and it creates similar sounding words that twist the tongue.

# Word History

4 to 15    3    Pencil and paper (for each player), a dictionary

 *To expand your vocabulary by coming up with amusing stories to explain the meanings of difficult words.*

1 Two players look up as many challenging words in the dictionary as there are players. Write these words down on a sheet of paper. Everyone swots up on what has been written down.

2 Players then take it in turns to look up the meaning of these words in the dictionary and reading out the individual definitions to the others.

3 Work together as a group to come up with stories that could explain the possible origin of these words. Get as creative as you like!

151

# Word Scramble (Anagrams)

 2 or more   3   Pencil and paper (for each player)

 *To rearrange jumbled-up words into real words from mixed-up letters.*

**1** Choose a word category – this could be animals, countries, colours, toys, etc. Everyone chooses three five-letter words to unscramble within the category. For example, 'sheep becomes 'peesh' or 'zebra' becomes 'braze'. Don't worry if these words look odd.

**2** Everyone writes down three words on their sheet of paper in large letters, but with the letters jumbled up.

**3** Everyone swaps sheets of paper with their neighbour.

**4** Race the other players to untangle the words that appear on your sheet while they try to unscramble the contents of theirs.

**5** Whoever is quickest to sort out the words given, or guesses the most correctly, is the winner and becomes the jumbler on the next round.

An anagram is a word whose letters can be rearranged to form a new word. You'll love this game if you like mixed-up letters!

152

# Synonyms

 2 or more     3    Pencil and paper (for each player), a watch or timer, a thesaurus or dictionary

 *To find as many synonyms for the words given as you can.*

1. Ask an adult to choose a list of 10 or 20 words. For example, 'lukewarm' and 'tepid' are synonyms of each other. These words must then be copied onto sheets of paper and handed out to each of the players.

2. Find a table or a flat writing surface. At the signal, write down as many synonyms as you can think of.

3. When 5 minutes are up, all players must hand in their sheets of paper and an adult checks them for accuracy using a thesaurus or a dictionary.

4. Tally up your score by counting the number of letters in the synonyms that you got right. The highest score belongs to the winner.

Lukewarm - ? ? ?

Synonyms are words with the same or similar meanings. They are the opposite of antonyms (see page 138).

# Hidden Words

 2 or more     3     Pencil and paper for each player, a watch or timer, a dictionary

 *To 'see' as many hidden words inside a bigger word as quickly as you can.*

**1** Everyone agrees a key word at least seven letters long. For example, 'kitchen'.

**2** Give yourself and the other players 5 minutes to study the word and come up with a series of mini words 'tucked away' inside the longer word. For example, inside the word 'kitchen', you can find shorter words like 'itch', 'it' and 'net'. Any new words must contain at least two letters, and you can only use the given letters once.

**3** Write down all the words you find.

**4** The player with the longest list of words is the winner. He or she gets to pick the next word and the game continues.

Good spelling ability is key in this game.

154

# Strategy Games

# Giant Slaying

😊 2    📦 1    📦 A sheet of graph paper, a pencil, 3 white counters (the 'dwarfs') and 1 black counter (the 'giant')

 To win, the white counters must trap the black counter in circle number 9. To win, the black counter must break behind their line and land on circle number 1.

1. Copy the game board shown below.

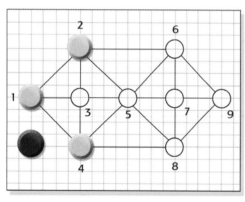

2. Place the white counters on circles 1, 2 and 4. The black counter can go on any of the circles, but you're not allowed to have more than one counter on a circle at a time.

3. The player with the white counters is first to play.

4. Players take it in turns to move each counter along the lines on the board towards any circles that are free. White counters can move sideways or forwards, but not backwards. The black counter, however, can be played in any direction.

5. The white counters win if they block the black counter in circle 9. The black counter wins if it reaches circle 1.

# The Star

 2     1     A sheet of graph paper, a pencil, 4 white counters, 4 black counters

 *To block all your opponent's counters so they cannot move.*

1. Copy the game board shown below.

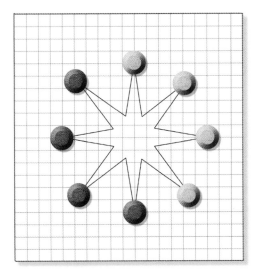

2. Place all eight counters on the tips of the arms of the star. The four black counters occupy the left arms. The four white counters occupy the right arms.

3. Draw lots or flip a coin to see who goes first.

4. A counter can move from the tip of the arm towards the middle (but only if one of the arms either side is already blocked by a counter of the opposite colour) or it can move from one arm of the star to the next if this space is free.

5. Two counters cannot be stacked in the same place on the game board.

6. The first player to block all of his or her opponent's counters is the winner.

# Fox and Geese

😊 2        📦 1        🛍️ 1 black counter, 13 white counters, graph paper and a pencil

 *If you control the single counter (the fox), to try and remove all of the geese from the board by jumping them. If you control the 13 counters (the geese), to prevent this by pinning down the fox so it cannot move.*

**1** Copy the cross-shaped game board shown below.

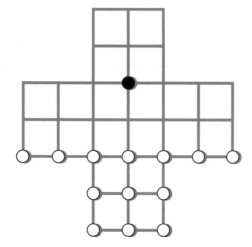

*This game is a good introduction to checkers, or draughts, which is a little bit more complicated. In it, the geese must work together to chase and trap the fox before they're captured. The wily fox must catch as many geese as it can to prevent it becoming trapped!*

**2** Place the counters as shown. The black counter represents the fox. The 13 white counters are the geese.

**3** Draw lots or flip a coin to decide who plays the black counter.

**4** One of the white counters makes the opening move.

**5** You and your opponent take it in turns to move your own counters forwards, backwards and sideways (but not diagonally).

**6** If you're the fox, your task is to break through the line of geese and gobble them up all the way to the back row. The fox can capture a goose by jumping over it to an empty square beyond. The counter must then be removed from the board. If there is the opportunity for a sequence of multiple hops, the fox can capture more than one goose in one go!

**7** If you're playing the geese, you cannot capture the fox, but you can corner it on all sides so it's unable to move in any direction!

# Two-Colour Snakes

 2     1     Graph paper, 2 coloured pencils

To stop your opponent's slithering snake in its tracks.

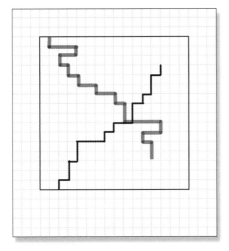

**4** You and your opponent take it in turns to start drawing your snakes from opposite sides of the paper.

**1** Box in a large grid (16 x 16 squares) on the graph paper.

**2** Each player is given a pencil.

**3** Draw lots or flip a coin to see who goes first.

**5** You start to draw a continuous line only by connecting one horizontal or vertical side of a square at a time – no more than that is allowed in one go.

**6** The first player to block his or her opponent's snake by touching it is the winner.

# Matchstick Pyramid

😊 2    📦 1    16 used safety matches (ask an adult to light and then blow them out before you use them)

To trick your opponent into picking up the last matchstick.

1. Build your pyramid in four rows. The bottom row has seven matchsticks; the second five; the third three; and the top row has one matchstick.

2. When it is your turn, remove one, two or three matchsticks from a row at a time.

3. The player who picks up the last remaining matchstick loses the game.

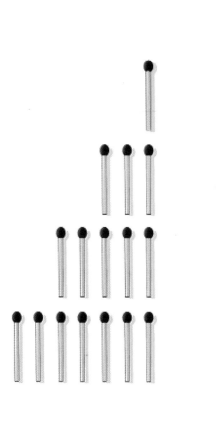

You can play with matchsticks anywhere, anytime because they are so light to carry and you can take them with you wherever you go!

# Seventeen Matches

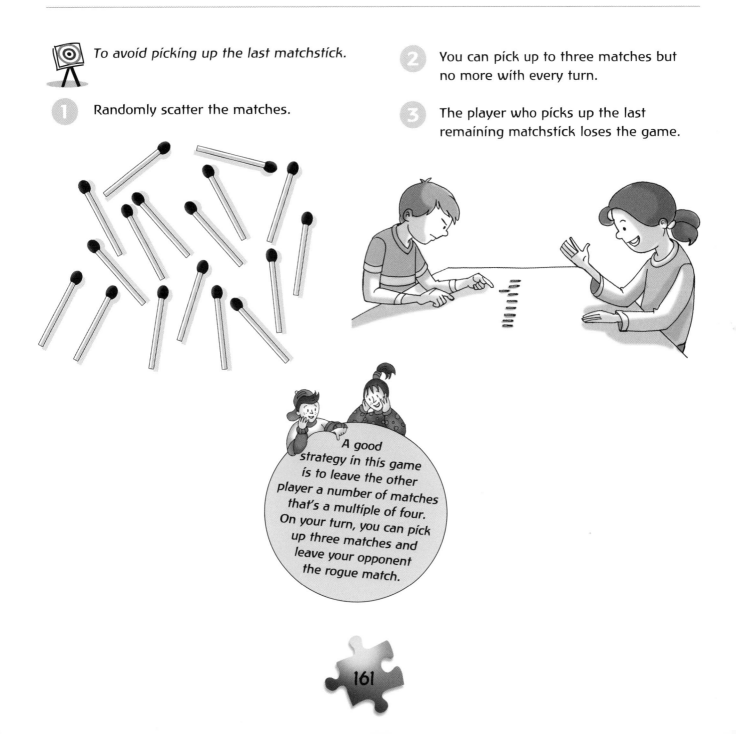

😊 2     📦 1     🎁 17 used safety matches (ask an adult to light and then blow them out before you use them)

🎯 *To avoid picking up the last matchstick.*

**2** You can pick up to three matches but no more with every turn.

**1** Randomly scatter the matches.

**3** The player who picks up the last remaining matchstick loses the game.

A good strategy in this game is to leave the other player a number of matches that's a multiple of four. On your turn, you can pick up three matches and leave your opponent the rogue match.

161

# Connect the Dots

 2 or more 　　2　　 Graph paper, a pencil or crayon (for each player)

To close off as many squares on the board as you can by completing boxes using horizontal or vertical connecting lines.

**1** Copy the grid shown. The number of dots doesn't matter, but make sure you have the same number of dots going across as going down.

**2** Each player is given a pencil or a crayon.

**3** Draw lots or flip a coin to see who goes first.

**4** Connect the first two dots with a vertical line.

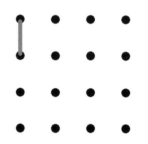

**5** When it's your opponent's turn, he or she connects another two dots with a horizontal line this time.

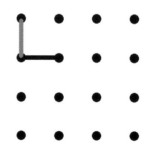

**6** As a follow-up to your opponent's move, connect one of these dots to a new dot with another vertical line.

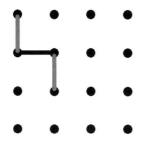

**7** Your opponent responds by connecting two more dots with a vertical line this time.

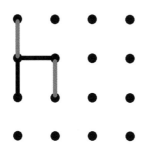

**8** When you close off the first box in the game, write your initials inside (shown here as AA). It's still your turn.

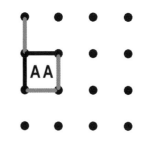

**9** Add another horizontal line to connect two more dots.

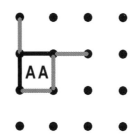

**10** Continue to play until the play grid is full and there's nowhere left to go.

**11** Whoever has the most boxes to his or name at the end of the game, wins.

# Battleships

😊 2    🪜 3    🛍️ A sheet of graph paper and a felt-tip pen (for each player)

◎ *To find and sink your opponent's navy*
*before your fleet is found and sunk.*

**1** Divide your sheet of paper into two
halves with two gaming grids – one at
the top and one at the bottom. Each grid
must measure 10 squares tall by 10
squares wide. Make sure that your
opponent's grid looks the same as yours.

**2** Label the first rows of squares running
along the top of both grids with the
letters A–J. Label the first rows of
squares running vertically down the
sides with the numbers 1 to 10.
This is your battleground.

**3** Mark the positions of your fleet in
the top grid: an aircraft carrier is
five squares in a straight line; two
battleships or destroyers are four
squares in a straight line; and five
submarines are a single square each.
Remember that the different ships can
be placed anywhere on the grid (either
horizontally or vertically) but their edges
may not touch.

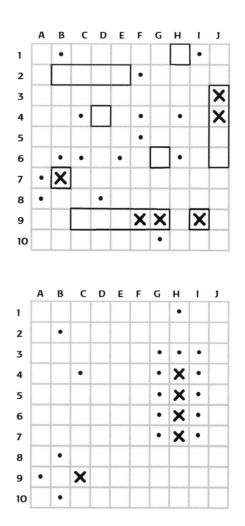

164

**4** You and your opponent take it in turns to call out different grid positions using a letter and a number. If, for example, he or she says B7, one of your four boats has been hit (see top diagram) and sunk as it only occupied one cell. You must

then reply 'hit and sunk', mark it with an 'X' and say which craft it was. In this case, the other player gets to have another go. If, for example, G3 was called out instead, you would say 'water' and it would be your turn.

**5** Record your opponent's hits and misses in the top grid. Mark any hits with an 'X' and misses with a dot. Record your hits and misses against your opponent's fleet in the bottom grid in the same way.

**6** The first player to sink all of his or her opponent's vessels is the winner.

This classic game of strategy lets you direct your own naval battle and play for your opponent's targets!

# Checkers (Draughts)

 2     3     A checker or chessboard, 12 white checkers, 12 black checkers, a piece of paper and a pencil (if you want to keep track of the score)

 *To capture all of your opponent's checkers, or block them so they cannot move.*

**1** Set up all 24 checkers on the first three rows of black squares on opposite sides of the board. If you're playing the black checkers, you move first.

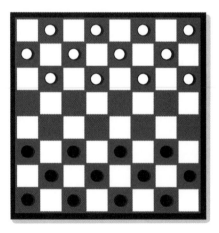

**2** Single checkers move forward diagonally, one square at a time. Each player takes it in turn to move one of his or her checkers.

**3** You can capture one of your opponent's checkers by jumping over it and landing your checker on the empty square beyond.

**4** If one of your checkers is next to one that belongs to your opponent and the square beyond it is free, you must jump over this checker. Remove it from the board.

**5** It's possible to do multiple jumps as well – the same checker can jump several times to capture more than one piece in a row, if there are vacant squares diagonally behind each.

**6** If you touch a checker, you have to move it. So, if you're not going to play it, remember not to touch it.

**7** When you move your checker to the last row on the opposite side of the board, that checker becomes a king. If you place another checker on top of it (to crown it) this piece can now move diagonally forward or backwards. You're allowed to jump as many of your opponent's checkers on the same move as possible.

**8** The player who first captures all of his or her opponent's pieces is the winner.

# 3-D Noughts and Crosses

 2    3    Paper and pencil, a ruler

 To score four symbols in a row across more than one face on a three-dimensional cube.

**1** Draw a cube. Divide each face into nine squares.

**2** Draw lots or flip a coin to decide who gets to be the noughts and who gets to be the crosses.

**3** You and your opponent take it in turns to mark one square at a time with either an 'O' (nought) or an 'X' (cross). You can strike through a line horizontally, vertically or diagonally. Your challenge is to stop your opponent from outsmarting you.

**4** If you line up four noughts (or crosses) across more than one cube face, you have beaten your opponent and are the winner.

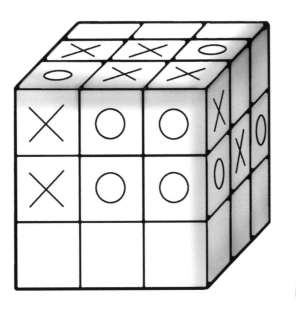

This solid game of strategy is a three-dimensional version of tic-tac-toe!

# Sprouts

2 or more    3    Paper, coloured pencils (optional), pens

To stop your opponent from making easy dot connections.

**1** Each player chooses a pencil or a pen.

**2** Draw two dots on a piece of paper.

**3** You and your opponent take it in turns to draw curved lines from one dot to another or from one dot to itself. Unlike *Connect the Dots* (see page 162), lines here can be any shape or size and shoot off in any direction! Remember to always put a dot on a new arc.

**4** Draw a curved line that begins and ends on the same dot. When you draw your new arc, add a dot.

**5** Your opponent connects this new dot and one of the two original dots (see step one) with a curved arc (plus a new dot). Notice that no new line can intersect or cross over an existing line or dot.

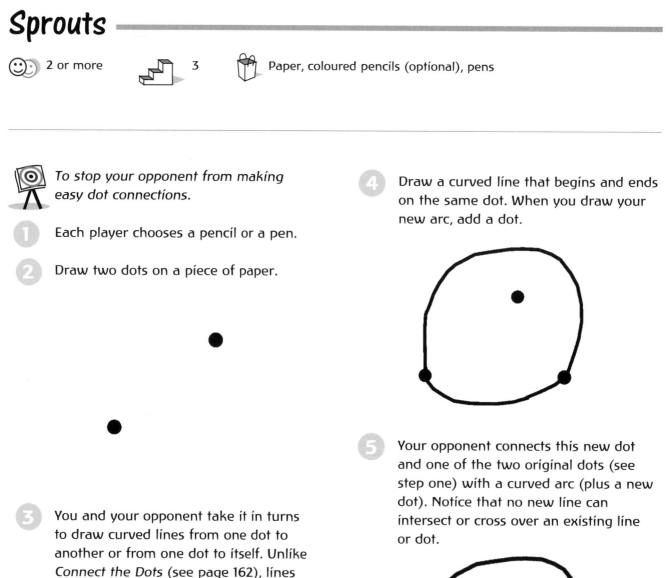

**6** Continue by connecting the new dot to one of the two original dots from step one. Note that no dot can have more than three lines coming out of it. Add a dot to your new arc.

**8** Draw an arc that joins up two existing dots. This last move leaves your opponent with nowhere to go as all the dots (except one) already have three lines coming out of them.

**7** Your opponent draws a circle through one of the two original dots then adds a dot to this arc. He or she is trying to close you off at this point, so look out!

**9** You win because your opponent is cornered and has no moves left!

As you'll see, the rules in sprouts are easy to grasp, but the strategy is more involved. Once you've mastered the basics, your 'board' could stretch anywhere between five to 30 dots!

# Halma

 2    3    10 white counters, 10 black counters, graph paper and a pencil (if you want to keep track of the score)

 *To move all your counters from your corner into the opposite corner of the board.*

1. Copy game and the board shown below.

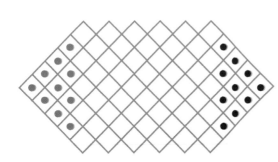

2. Position the white and black counters on opposite corners of the board.

3. You and your opponent take it in turns to move your own counters. On each turn, you can move a counter into the adjacent square or, if possible, hop over another counter into the square beyond,

and so on. The game starts to become interesting when there are lots of counters in the middle of the board.

4. Counters can move forwards, backwards and diagonally. A single counter can also make multiple hops over several other counters and quickly move across the board.

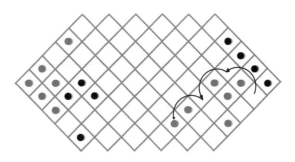

5. No counters may be captured or removed.

6. You can jump over your own counters as well as those of the other player.

7. The first player to move all of his or her counters into the opponent's corner is the winner.

This challenging game of strategy was originally played on a huge game board that was 16 squares x 16 squares (256 squares in total). Just think, a standard chess or checkerboard only has 64!

# Tabletop Games

# Tiddlywinks

 4 or more          2          4 sets of 4 plastic tiddlywinks (each set must be a different colour), 1 larger tiddlywink as a shooter, a cup or a plate

*To flip as many of your tiddlywinks into the cup using the shooter and lots of crafty moves.*

**1** Place the cup in the middle of a table, or the floor. If you're using a plate, aiming will be easier. If you and the other players are sharp shots, a cup should guarantee bigger thrills!

**2** Each player is given a set of four colour tiddlywinks.

**3** Sit around in a circle and take turns trying to flip the tiddlywinks into the bowl, one by one. Opening shots should be about 20 metres (or from 65 feet) from the cup or plate.

**4** To make your tiddlywink 'jump', simply press down on the edge of it with your shooter and watch it fly through the air!

**5** If your tiddlywink lands in the plate or cup, you 'pot the wink' and get to have another go. If not, it is the next player's turn to take a shot.

You can also buy a cloth or plastic sheet with rings and a central bullseye target with points on it. To set up your game, simply place a cup in the middle of it.

**6** If one tiddlywink lands on top of another, that bottom tiddlywink is 'squopped'. You have effectively stopped that piece from being played until you decide you move your top tiddlywink – a good delay tactic against your opponent! So long as the bottom tiddlywink remains covered, it cannot score points for your opponent.

**7** Any tiddlywinks lying around the cup area at the end of one round will be flipped on the next round from the point where they landed.

**8** The first player to pot all his or her tiddlywinks is the winner.

173

# Jacks

 1 or more     2     A set of jacks (10 metal jacks, 2 extras and a rubber ball)

 *This game requires a variety of skills – concentration, speed, good hand-eye coordination – to scoop up as many jacks as you can.*

**1** Find a smooth, flat surface like a table or the pavement. Sit or crouch down.

**2** Toss a handful of 10 jacks on the ground. If there are two or more players, decide who goes first: each player takes a turn balancing the jacks on the back of his or her hand before tossing them up and trying to catch as many as possible. Whoever gets the most jacks has the first go.

**3** In the first round, pick up one jack at a time during each toss. Throw the rubber ball into the air, let the ball bounce once and pick up the jack with your throwing hand. (Be generous and allow a player who is new to the game a double bounce.) As you pick up the jacks, catch the ball with the same hand. Try and throw the ball straight up in the air but not too high.

**4** Transfer the jack to your other hand. Repeat step three until all jacks have been picked up.

**5** In the second round, pick up two jacks at a time during each toss until all the jacks have been collected.

**6** In the third round, pick up groups of three jacks during each toss. Repeat this three times until there is only one jack left to pick up. Scoop up the last jack.

**7** Remember that leftover jacks may occur in groups of fours, sixes, sevens, eights and nines on the various rounds.

**8** Continue playing until you get to the tenth round. Pick up all 10 jacks in one go.

**9** If your opponent makes a mistake by failing to pick up the correct number of jacks, drops one or more jacks, or picks up after more than one ball bounce, it's your turn. You begin the next turn with the number you last failed on.

Did you know that the game of jacks was originally played using the knucklebones of sheep?

# Dominoes

2    2    A standard set of 28 dominoes

To lay down as many dominoes as possible by matching the number of dots on their faces.

**1** Find a table or another flat surface like the floor. Place all 28 dominoes face-down and mix them up.

**2** Each player draws one domino from this 'bone pile'. Whoever gets the highest-scoring ('heaviest') domino goes first.

**3** Each player draws seven dominoes from the 'bone pile'.

**4** Set up your hand in a row with the seven pieces standing upright so no one else can see their value.

**5** If you're the first player, lay any domino face-up in the middle of the table. The person to your left goes next.

176

**6** He or she selects a domino piece from his or her hand. It must have the same number of dots on one side as the piece on the table.

**7** When you're making the numbers match, place your domino against another piece so that the ends with the same number of dots are touching.

**8** Any player with a double can play one end of this (or any other matching) domino but must place their 'double' domino across the bottom of the original piece in a T-shape. This is how you build up the famous domino pattern.

**9** If you have no matches for what's on the table, keep drawing from the 'bone pile' until you find a piece that you can play.

**10** The next player takes a turn and plays a matching piece or draws from the 'bone pile' as well, and so on.

**11** If the player before you has played a double, you can continue the layout by jumping over the 'T' in the pattern or playing off in one of the directions of the 'T'.

**12** Whoever gets rid of all his or her dominoes first is the winner. If the 'bone pile' runs out before anyone has used up all their pieces, the player with the lowest number of dots wins.

Get ready to match up numbers in this classic tabletop challenge. These flat, rectangular tiles are usually black but also come in white. One face is divided by a line with one, two, three, four, five, six dots or a blank space on either side of it. The dots either side of the line are called 'suits'. Pieces with an equal number of dots on either side of the line are called one-number suits and are doubles. There are seven of these in a standard 28-tile set. The remaining 21 dominoes are mixed suits with a different number of dots on either side of the line, or dots on one side and a blank on the other.

178

# Pick-Up Sticks

 2 or more    3    40 thin pencil sticks (25 centimetres or about 10 inches in length), red, blue, yellow and green paint, a pencil sharpener, a paintbrush

 *To pull out as many sticks as you can during your turn without moving the others in the pile – easier said than done!*

**1** Sharpen each pencil end using the sharpener. Paint 20 yellow, 12 red, five blue, three green and the other two with spirals in a colour of your choice. The pick-up sticks should end up looking like huge, colour toothpicks.

**2** At the start of the game, grasp all the sticks in both hands, keeping them vertical to the hard surface of a desk or a table. Set the bottom of one hand on the table so that the sticks rise straight up. Open your other hand and gently let the sticks fall.

**3** Players take in turns to try to pick up one of the sticks without shifting the others in the pile. If the stick you're trying to pull out moves something else even by a fraction, it's the next player's turn. If their luck holds out, they'll keep on pulling out sticks until the pile finally jiggles.

**4** Players can only tally up their score once all sticks have been removed. Yellow sticks are worth 3 points; red sticks are worth 5 points; blue sticks are worth 10 points; green sticks are worth 15 points; and the spiral ones (where the big points are at) are each worth 20!

This game requires a steady hand, concentration and a high tolerance for frustration!

# Pick-Up Toothpicks

2 or more      3      A box of toothpicks

To pick up the last toothpick on the table using some serious strategic manoeuvres.

**1** Find a table or another flat surface.

**2** Use any number of toothpicks.

**3** Divide them up into as many piles as you want. You don't have to count the number of toothpicks in each pile – this doesn't matter.

**4** You and your opponent take turns picking up one, some or all the toothpicks in one pile. But here's the twist – when it's your turn, you can also choose to *divide* an existing pile into two or more piles instead.

**5** Players cannot pick up pieces from more than one pile or divide more than one pile in a single turn.

**6** Try to think several moves ahead of your opponent. For example, if there are two piles on the table, you might not want to pick up one pile in one go because your opponent can then pick up the other and win the game. It's a better gaming tactic, for example, to pick up *some* of one pile or divide it up further into two piles or more.

**7** The player who's left with the final move is the winner.

Did you know that Nim (see page 130) was originally played with piles of stones instead of wooden toothpicks?

180

# Card Games

# Old Maid

3 to 6      1      A standard deck of 52 cards

*To collect card pairs and avoid the old maid (queen of spades).*

1. Find a table or another flat surface on which to play.

2. Take out the other three queens from the deck but leave in the queen of spades (the old maid).

3. Everyone picks a card. Whoever selects the highest card gets to be the dealer. If you're the dealer, shuffle the deck and deal the cards, face down, one at a time, to the other players. Some players might get more cards than others – this is normal in the game.

4. Players look at their hands (the cards they've been dealt), pull out any matching pairs (in terms of rank) and lay down any matches in a pile next to them.

5. If you draw a card that matches the one in your hand, lay the pair in a pile face up. If you have no pair, play continues with the player to your left. If you have three cards that match in number, put two down and keep the third. If you have four cards, you can put down two pairs.

6. After everyone has finished laying down their matches, the first player to your left fans out his or her hand, keeping the faces hidden. The player to this person's left picks out a card and hopes to match it with what is in his or her hand. Any matches go in the pile.

7. Play goes around in a circle with players picking cards from each other and laying down matches.

8. There is only one old maid card, and it can never make a pair. Whoever has it can therefore never win the game!

9. The first player who ends up empty-handed, wins.

10. The player left holding the queen of spades in his or her hand is the (very) unlucky loser!

182

Success in this game is about pure luck and has nothing to do with skill. It's a level playing field from the start.

# Snap

😊 2 to 4    📦 1    🎁 A standard deck of 52 cards

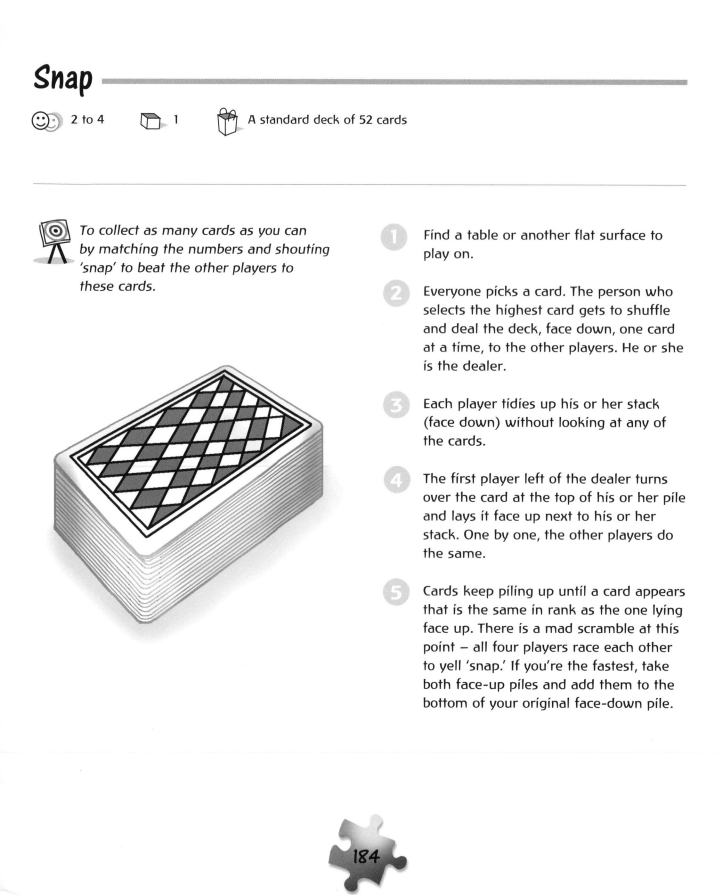

🎯 *To collect as many cards as you can by matching the numbers and shouting 'snap' to beat the other players to these cards.*

**1** Find a table or another flat surface to play on.

**2** Everyone picks a card. The person who selects the highest card gets to shuffle and deal the deck, face down, one card at a time, to the other players. He or she is the dealer.

**3** Each player tidies up his or her stack (face down) without looking at any of the cards.

**4** The first player left of the dealer turns over the card at the top of his or her pile and lays it face up next to his or her stack. One by one, the other players do the same.

**5** Cards keep piling up until a card appears that is the same in rank as the one lying face up. There is a mad scramble at this point – all four players race each other to yell 'snap.' If you're the fastest, take both face-up piles and add them to the bottom of your original face-down pile.

**6** The game continues to the left of the player who turned up the matching card.

**7** If you shout 'snap' at the wrong time, you give one of your cards to each player.

**8** When two or more players yell 'snap' together, the matching card piles are stacked up in the middle of the table in a central snap pool.

**9** The game continues as before, but the first player to call out 'snap pool' when someone turns over a card that matches the one on top of the middle pile gets to collect these cards as well.

**10** When you've used up all your face-down cards, you can start to use the ones in the face-up pile.

**11** Whoever runs out of cards before the game is over is out.

**12** The winner collects all the cards.

This number-matching card game is very easy to learn and loads of fun to play!

# Slapjack

😊 2 to 5    📦 1    🎁 A standard deck of 52 cards

🎯 *To win all of the cards by quickly recognizing the jacks when they appear before another card gets slapped down on top.*

**1** Find a table or another flat surface on which to play. Put the deck on the table in front of you.

**2** Everyone picks a card. Whoever selects the highest card is the dealer. He or she shuffles and deals the deck, face down, one card at a time, to the other players. Some players might get more cards than others – this is normal.

**3** Place all of your cards face down. Every other player does the same.

**4** If you're to the dealer's left you go first. Turn over the top card from your pile in front of everyone. The player to your left then places his or her card face up on top of your original card. As the game continues, new cards are always being added to this central pile until someone lays down a jack.

**5** As soon you see the jack, slap your hand down on it before someone else does. If you beat the other players to it, take the pile of cards underneath the jack. Mix it with your pile.

**6** The player to your left starts a new pile of cards in the middle of the table. If you jump the gun and slap another card by mistake, you have to give one of your cards to each of the other players.

**7** Whoever runs out of cards before the game is over is out.

**8** The first player to collect all cards is the winner.

*You must have lightning-fast reactions and the eyes of a hawk to slap down the jack and win all the cards lying underneath!*

186

# Fifteen

 1    2    A standard deck of 52 cards, plus jokers

*To be an ace at this game of skilled calculation, you must select any number of random cards to try to score 15 points as often as you can until all the cards in the reserve pile have been used up.*

**1** Sit at a table. Shuffle the deck and deal out 16 cards in four rows, face down, four cards to a row. The remaining cards go in a reserve pile to one side.

**2** From the 16 cards that are laid out face down on the table, turn over many cards as you need to obtain 15 points (or as close to this score as possible). Do this as many times as you can. You cannot go over a score of 15 points or you have lost.

The value of the different cards is as follows:

- joker (15 points)

- king (13 points)

- queen (12 points)

- jack (11 points)

- other cards are worth the number of points they represent (for example, the 10 of spades is worth 10 points, and so on).

**3** Cards that are used up go in a waste pile. As you play, replace them with cards from the reserve pile and continue to play until you are unable to collect 15 points from the cards that are left over. See how long your luck holds out!

# Go Fish

 2 to 6    2    A standard deck of 52 cards

*To collect as many groups of four matching cards as you can. For example, if you had two queens in your hand, you would ask whether anyone else had queens. Remember you cannot ask for a matching card unless you already hold one in your hand.*

**1** Find a table or another flat surface on which to play. Put the deck on the table in front of you.

**2** Everyone picks a card. Whoever selects the highest card gets to be the dealer.

**3** Each player receives seven cards (or five, if there are four players or more) face down from the dealer. The remaining cards are spread face down out on the table. They make up

Get ready to fish for your lucky cards in this fun card-matching game. Remember, though, that picking up cards in this way is a bit of a gamble – you might not get a valuable card.

the 'pond' from where players will have to dip for cards during the course of the game.

**4** Everyone inspects their hand (the cards they've been dealt) and arranges them by rank next to each other. Remember: you're trying to collect as many groups of four matching cards of the same rank as you can.

**5** The player left of the dealer goes first and asks the others for the cards that he or she needs to fill out a group of four. If someone has any of these cards, he or she must turn them over and give them to the player on the dealer's left, who gets to go again. This player again asks the others for cards. If there are no matches, this player has to draw a card from the 'fishing pond' in the middle and add it to his or her hand. His or her turn is over.

**6** It's now the turn of the second player to the dealer's left. Players take it in turns to ask for cards that will fill out their books (say, for example, four queens). If these cards are not available from other players, you draw from the 'pond' and add it to your hand.

**7** If you choose a useless card, it's the next person's turn. If you get a valuable card, you cry, 'I fished and I got my wish' because your turn is not yet over.

**8** Pay attention to what other players are asking for, as this could give you the edge when your turn comes around again.

**9** When you've collected four matching cards, lay them face up on the table for everyone to see.

**10** The winner is the first person to end up with no cards in his or her hands.

# War

😊 2     ⬒ 2     🛍 A standard deck of 52 cards, watch or timer

🎯 *To capture all of your opponent's cards.*

**1** Find a table or another flat surface on which to play. Set the timer.

**2** You and your opponent each pick a card. The person who selects the higher card gets to shuffle and deal out the deck, face down, one card at a time.

**3** You and your opponent place your cards in a pile, face down, in front of each other.

**4** Turn your top cards over together and place them face up and side by side in the middle. (Remember that aces are high-scoring cards in this game.)

**5** If you play the higher-ranking card, you get to keep both cards (and vice versa).

**6** Collect these cards and add them to the bottom of your stack.

**7** If you both turn over cards of the same rank, you declare 'war' on each other and the fun part begins.

**8** Each one of you places the three top cards from your pile face down on top of the card you have just declared war with.

**9** Each one of you then places a fourth card on top of the three cards, face up. The higher face-up cards wins all the cards. If your cards and those of your opponent match once again, it's 'double war'.

**10** The card battle continues until the winner captures all 52 cards. You can also win if your opponent runs out of cards.

Why win one battle when you can win the whole war? Do make sure you give yourself a time limit as this game of chance can carry on for ages!

# Chase the Ace

5 or more     2     A standard deck of 52 cards, 3 counters (for example, pennies or buttons) for each player

*To get rid of the ace (the lowest card).*

**1** Everyone picks a card. Whoever selects the highest card deals the first hand. He or she is the dealer.

**2** The dealer hands each player three counters (each one represents a 'life' in the game).

**3** Everyone puts a 'stake' (a quantity of their counters – not all!) in the pot (to be collected by the winner of that round).

**4** Each player is dealt one card face down by the dealer. Everyone looks at their card and decides whether they want to keep it or trade it (if it is a low-ranking card) when it is their turn. Any undealt cards are left in a pile on the table.

**5** The player left of the dealer goes first and play continues around the table in a clockwise direction. Each player can either keep a card ('stand') or trade it with the first person to their left and hope for a better one ('change'). The player who has just been forced to trade decides whether to 'stand' or 'change', and so on. Changing a card is a big risk – unless you already hold an ace, it is very likely you will end up with a lower card. If you trade and the new card is an ace, a 2 or a 3, you must tell the other players.

**6** To trade a card, simply slide it face down over to player on your left. This person has to accept the swap unless he or she has a king, in which case the card is exposed and you must trade with the next player over. Players continue to be on the lookout for aces as these will keep moving around the table.

**7** The dealer's turn comes last and he or she cannot trade with anyone. To trade, he or she buries the card in the middle of the deck and chooses another card from the top of the pile and shows it to the other players. If you've picked a king and are the dealer, for example, you lose your hand and one counter.

**8** The other players' cards are revealed. The player with the lowest card loses a counter.

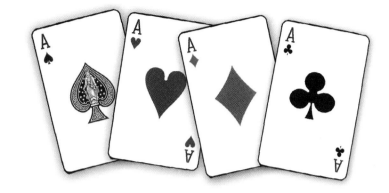

**9** If two players or more tie for the lowest card, each loses a life.

**10** The player on the original dealer's left now becomes the dealer in the second round. Cards from the last round are added to the bottom of the deck and another hand is dealt.

**11** Any player who loses all three lives is out of the game.

**12** The last player with one remaining counter wins and collects the rewards in the pot.

What happens if both or all of the players that are left over tie for the lowest card, so they're all out of the game? Choose your favourite solution:

**a** They become joint winners and split the pot between them.

**b** They get to keep their last 'life' and another deal is played out between them.

**c** As the game result is undecided, the pot is carried forward to the next game with each player adding a new stake to it.

In this betting-and-trading game, kings are high and aces are low. Suits don't count, and the cards rank in this order: king (high), queen, jack, 10, 9, 8, 7, 6, 5, 4, 3, 2, ace (low). Enjoy the thrill of collecting a pot after a winning round!

# Rummy

😊 2 to 6    📶 3    🎁 A standard deck of 52 cards

🎯 *To get rid of all your cards. To do this, you must find and collect certain card combinations (known as 'melds') and lay off as many of your opponents' card combinations as possible.*

1. Find a table or another flat surface on which to play. Place the card deck in front of you.

2. Everyone picks a card. The person who selects the highest card gets to shuffle and deal one card at a time, face down, to you and the others. He or she is the dealer. With two players playing, you each get 10 cards. If there are three to four players, each person receives seven cards; if there are five or six people around the table, each gets six cards.

3. Place the remaining cards in a stock pile face down in the middle of the table. Turn the top card face up and set it down by the first stack as a waste pile.

4. To win, try and collect as many melds as you possibly can – they will obviously change and have to be adjusted during the course of the game, depending on which cards everyone else is trying to collect.

5. The player to the dealer's left picks up the top card from either the stock pile or the waste pile. He or she discards any card from his or her hand onto the waste pile.

6. If you pick a card from this pile, you cannot put down the same card.

7. The game continues in a clockwise direction with each player picking up and discarding a card on their turn.

8. When you have a meld, you can either hold back or lay them face up on the table in full view of the other players who can lay off their cards onto your melds by adding a fourth card to a three-of-a-kind or to the high or low end of a three-in-a-row sequence.

9. Try to lay off as many cards as you can when it's your turn.

10. When the stock pile runs out and a player refuses the top card from the waste pile, flip it over and play it as new stock. Try to win your hand by playing all your cards, but you don't have to discard them when you go out unless you want to.

**11** The first hand is scored, and the value of all the cards that are left over in the other players' hands are also added to it.

Cards are worth as follows:

- **Aces** – 1 point
- **Face cards, such as the jack, queen and king** – 10 points
- **Number cards** – their number value

**12** The second hand is shuffled and dealt by the player on the dealer's left, and so on.

**13** The game continues until a player reaches the points target that was decided before the game began, or until the agreed number of deals has been played.

There are probably more versions of rummy out there than any other card game. Players must have good strategic thinking and be able to rethink tactics while they watch the other players closely.

195

### Tips for playing rummy

- On each turn, try doubling your score early on by putting out all your cards (going rummy). To do this, you cannot have laid out any melds or laid off any cards on your opponents' melds up to that point.

- Discard unwanted face cards.

- During any hand, watch how your opponents are playing their hands and try not to discard cards that might be useful to the player on your left. Start keeping track of which cards others need and avoid helping them out.

- Don't be afraid to change your gaming strategy halfway through if you start to notice that others seem to snatching up all the cards you need – who knows, they might be onto you, too! For maximum success, keep a clear head and be prepared to keep changing the groups and sequences that you're after…

- Remember to try and keep the hand winner's score low by not holding onto high-ranking cards at the end of a hand.

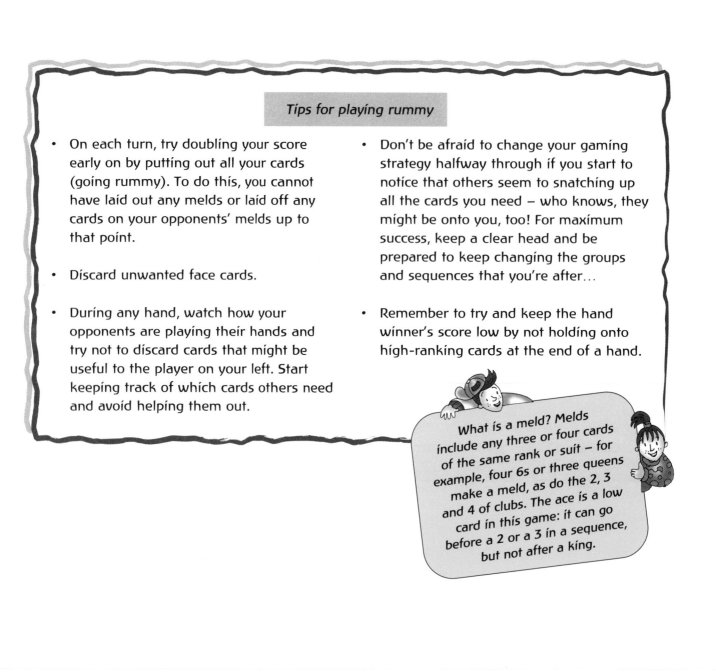

What is a meld? Melds include any three or four cards of the same rank or suit – for example, four 6s or three queens make a meld, as do the 2, 3 and 4 of clubs. The ace is a low card in this game: it can go before a 2 or a 3 in a sequence, but not after a king.

# Concentration

😊 3 or more     📶 3     🎁 A standard deck of 52 cards

🎯 *To find as many pairs of matching cards in terms of rank, but ignoring suit.*

**1** Lay all the cards face down and side by side in neat, even rows so they make a large rectangle.

**2** Players take it in turns to flip over two cards at a time. Try to match two in rank, regardless of suit. If you find a matching pair, you keep them and it's still your turn. If you're unlucky, flip the two cards back down again. It's now your opponent's turn.

**3** When it's someone else's turn, pay close attention to which cards are being exposed and what their location is. When it comes to your turn, start by flipping over those pairs that you remember seeing before trying to find new pairs.

**4** As more and more cards are removed from the display, it becomes easier to remember where the pairs are. The game can really pick up speed at this point!

**5** When all of the cards have been used up, the player with the most pairs wins.

**6** You might want to try a more challenging version. The aim now is to pick up only those pairs of cards that are the same in rank and colour (for example, a 7 of clubs and a 7 of spades). Are you up for it?

Try to remember the location of the pairs you have already turned over.

197

# Russian Bank

😊 2     🪜 3     🎁 2 standard playing decks (52 cards each), one for each player

🎯 *To get rid of all the cards from your hand, waste and reserve piles. You do this by playing your cards to the centre piles or tableau, and by loading them onto your opponent's reserve and waste piles.*

**1** Each player has a complete deck of cards. Deal all your cards from your *own* deck.

**2** Deal a pile of 12 cards, face down. Place another card face up on top to make 13. This is your reserve pile. Place it to your right.

**3** Deal another four cards, face up, in a neat column above the reserve pile. These are your four houses. Your opponent will have also dealt four houses. Together, the eight houses make up the tableau. From these cards, you and your opponent will build eight centre piles from aces. During the game, both the tableau and the centre piles are

common areas of play. Keep your layout really tidy so you can both clearly see how the game is going!

**4** Place the 35 cards left over face down on your left. These cards make up your

YOUR OPPONENT'S RESERVE PILE — YOUR OPPONENT'S WASTE PILE — YOUR OPPONENT'S HAND PILE

FOUR HOUSES — CENTRE PILES — TABLEAU — CENTRE PILES — FOUR HOUSES

YOUR HAND PILE — YOUR WASTE PILE — YOUR RESERVE PILE

*This game is an engaging and competitive patience card game for two players. In France, it's known as 'crapette'.*

hand pile. Your waste pile, which will grow as you play, goes between your hand and your reserve piles.

**5** Whoever has the lowest top reserve card begins play (remember: kings are high and aces are low). If there's a tie with the reserve cards, compare your first house cards. The lowest house card plays first. If there's a tie, continue with the second, and so on.

**6** Take it in turns to play until one of you is left with no reserve, waste or hand cards.

**7** During your turn, you're allowed to move your cards around the game layout, but you must do this according to a strict set of rules:

- *Playing the available cards:*
  The top card of your reserve pile (which is face up) and the cards furthest out in each of the eight houses of the tableau. Your move consists of taking a single available card and playing it, one at a time, to any of the eight centre piles, any of the eight houses in the tableau or your partner's reserve or waste pile.

- *Playing the centre piles:*
  You can only fill a space with an available ace. To build up each of the eight piles, add cards of the same suit in *ascending* order (lowest to highest): for example, ace , 2, 3, 4, 5, 6, 7, 8, 9, 10, jack, queen, king. For instance, the only card that can be placed on a 4 of clubs is a 5 of clubs, and no card can be added after the king.

- *Playing the tableau houses:*
  Build up these cards in *descending* order (highest to lowest) with alternating colours (red suit on black suit). For example, a 7 of hearts (red) can be played on *either* an 8 of spades (black) or an 8 of clubs (also black). To see the whole sequence, lay your cards down so they overlap. You can fill an empty house with any available card. As play continues, you will be adding cards to the houses in overlapping rows that extend away from the eight original centre piles.

Loading up an opponent's reserve or waste pile is a dicey move – be careful because it might not work to your advantage later on in the game!

- *Playing the reserve and waste piles:*
  Load your opponent's reserve or waste pile by adding a card of the same suit as the exposed card, of the higher or next lower rank. For example, if the top card is the 9 of diamonds, you can place an available card of 8 or 10 of diamonds on it. Having chosen to play the 8 of diamonds, for example, you would continue by adding the 7 of diamonds or a second 9 of diamonds.

**8** At each turn, make as many moves as you can or wish to. You can be stopped either when you have played out all the available options or you make a mistake by not following the rules of the game. If an available card is 'playable' from the tableau to the centre piles, it must be moved there *before* you can turn any of your hand cards over.

**9** If there's a gap in the tableau, you must fill it with a reserve card *before* you turn over and play any hand cards.

**10** When there are no moves with available cards left and you've finished playing the last card from your reserve pile, turn to the top card of your hand. If you don't want to play this card, put it in the waste pile. If it fits one of the centre piles, your opponent can make you play it there and then.

**11** When there are no cards left in your hand pile, turn over the top card from your waste pile. Try to play it as you move as many cards around as you can. As you play, continue to take cards from your waste pile. If you cannot play a card, place it to one side in the reserve pile, face up.

**12** Once the waste pile has been used up, the reserve pile is flipped over and becomes the waste pile.

**13** If, at this point, you cannot play any of your cards, your opponent takes all the cards in your hand pile.

**14** If you catch your opponent making mistakes – moving cards that are not available, placing a card somewhere it does not belong or turning up cards from other piles when his or her reserve is not yet empty – call 'stop' and you take over.

As a general rule, you cannot move cards *from*:

- your own waste pile
- your opponent's hand, waste or reserve pile
- any centre pile.

As a general rule, you cannot move cards *to*:

- your hand or the hand of the other player
- your reserve
- your waste pile, except when placing one of your hand cards there to end your turn.

**15** The player who gets rid of all the cards from his or her reserve, stock and waste piles is the winner.

If you love games like solitaire or patience, you'll find this game takes you to new challenging levels of fun, concentration, tactics and frustration!

# Dice Games

# Little Pig

 2 or more     1     Pencil and paper (for each player), coloured crayons, 2 dice

With a little luck, you may be the first to finish your drawing.

To draw/colour in the eye, 2.
To draw/colour in the snout, 3.
To draw/colour in the ears, 4.
To draw/colour in the legs, 5.
To draw/colour in the tail, 6. You really need to think lucky if you're to finish the drawing of your pig at all!

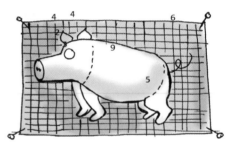

**1** Look at the drawing of the pig. Each part of it corresponds to a number. You can only draw the part that corresponds to the number that comes up on each throw of the dice when it is your turn.

**2** To be able to draw/colour in the body of the pig, you must throw a dice combination that adds up to 9.

**3** For example, if you've drawn in all parts except the tail, you must score 6 on the next throw if you can, otherwise your opponent could have better luck and beat you to it!

**4** The first player to complete their animal is the winner.

# Nifty Fifty

😊 2 or more    🎲 1    🎁 2 dice, pencil and paper (for scores)

 *To be the first player to reach 50 points by rolling two dice.*

**1** Find a table or another flat surface. Make sure all players are sitting down.

**2** Roll a die beforehand to see who starts the game. If you obtain the highest number, you get to go first. Whoever has the second highest score gets to go second, and so on. A tie is broken by another roll of the die.

**3** Players take it in turns to shoot the dice and aim for doubles.

**4** The rolls are worth as follows: all dice doubles score 5 points (except 3s and 6s); double 6s are worth a whopping 25 points so, obviously, trying to aim for these is a smart move. Very important: avoid unlucky double 3s if you can, as they wipe out your score up to that point and you have to restart.

**5** Use pencil and paper to keep track of each other's scores.

**6** The game continues with each participant taking one roll on every turn.

**7** The first player to achieve a score of 50 points or over is the winner.

As a general rule of thumb, try to roll dice doubles (the same number on each cube face) to get ahead in this game but avoid rolling two 3s!

# Lucky Dice

😊 2 or more    🎲 1    🎁 2 dice, pencil and paper (for scores)

🎯 To roll the 11 possible dice combinations in the right order.

**1** Find a table or another flat surface. Make sure all players are sitting down.

**2** Roll a die beforehand to see who starts the game. If you obtain the highest number, you get to go first. Whoever has the second highest score gets to go second, and so on. A tie is broken by another roll of the die.

**3** Players take it turns to shoot all possible dice combinations in sequence (2, 3, 4, 5, 6, 7, 8, 9, 10, 11, 12). For example, on the first roll of the dice, you would be looking to get two 1s (worth 2 points).

**4** The first round ends when all the players have had a chance to roll for the 2s.

**5** On each successive round, individual players try to roll for the 3, 4, 5, 6, and so on until they get to the 12.

**6** The correct combination is awarded points every time and is worth the same

One of the simplest dice games ever, it's down to pure luck and the roll of the dice in your hand!

number of points as its number. For example, the 6 (within the correct sequence) is worth 6 points.

7 Combinations of dice numbers that add up to the desired score are also allowed. For example, it's OK to roll two 3s, or a 4 and a 2, or a 5 and a 1 if you're aiming to achieve the 6 combination in the sequence.

8 Each player adds up his or her points.

9 The player with the highest total wins.

# The Racing Clock

😊 3 or 4    ⬚ 2    🎁 2 dice

 To go 'around the clock' by rolling numbers 1 to 12 in the correct order.

**1** Find a table or another flat surface. Make sure all players are sitting down.

**2** Roll a die beforehand to see who starts the game. If you obtain the highest number, you get to go first. Whoever has the second highest score gets to go second, and so on. A tie is broken by another roll of the die.

**3** Roll the dice once, aiming to get 1 on both faces. If you're unlucky, you'll have to hope for better luck next time as you wait for your turn again. If you roll successfully, you can shoot for a 2 on your next turn. What's really exciting is that you can try to get a 2 in one of two ways: either on a single die, or with the right combination of dice.

**4** If you get this total, you can shoot for 3 at your next turn, gradually working your way up to 12 during the course of the game. Like the hands on a clock!

**5** If luck's on your side and you manage to score two of the numbers that you need for the sequence with a single roll, you can count them both. For example, if you're aiming for the 5 in the sequence, rolling both a 5 and a 6 at the same time count. Then, at your next turn, you can skip straight to 7!

**6** After 6, it's obvious you need to roll a combination of dice for numbers 7 to 12.

**7** The game continues with you and your opponent taking it in turns until one player manages to complete going 'around the clock' before the others.

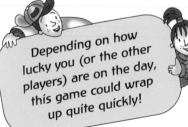 Depending on how lucky you (or the other players) are on the day, this game could wrap up quite quickly!

# Multiplication Dice

 3 or more     3     3 dice, pencil and paper (for scores)

*To score the highest possible score by rolling not two but three dice. There is a twist, however…*

**1** Find a table or another flat surface. Make sure all players are sitting down.

**2** Roll a die beforehand to see who starts the game. If you obtain the highest number, you get to go first. Whoever has the second highest score gets to go second, and so on. A tie is broken by another roll of the die.

**3** Roll the three dice in one throw and put the one that scores the highest to one side. If the highest number comes up on two dice, set one die aside. If the same number comes up on all three dice though, select only one die. The two remaining dice get rolled again and the highest-scoring die gets chosen. The last die is now rolled.

**4** To tally up your score, add the numbers on the first two dice and multiply this sum by the value of the third die. For example, if you get a 3 and 4 on the first two dice and a 5 on the third, you do a quick calculation like this:

$(3 + 4) \times 5$

Your score is 35 points because you add up the first two numbers and get 7, then multiply it by 5 to get 35.

**5** You can play this game for however many rounds you wish, but remember to always keep an eye on the score.

**6** The player with the highest total score is the winner.

*Look out for the power of the third roll. It's very unpredictable and can make or break a player in the last stages of this game!*

207

# Unlucky Dice

 2 or more     3     5 dice, pencil and paper (for scores)

 *To collect as many points as possible as you get rid of the 'unlucky' dice.*

**1** Find a table or another flat surface. Make sure both players are sitting down.

**2** Roll a die beforehand to see who starts the game. The player with the lowest score gets to go first this time. If there's a tie, break it with another roll of the die.

**3** Players take turns rolling all five dice. If no 2 or 5 comes up, you can add up the numbers on the faces of the five dice to get your score. These are the points scored on a single roll.

**4** If either a 2 or a 5 (or both) come up, you score nothing and must remove the 'unlucky' die or dice before the next roll. You could also have rolled 'lucky' and kept all five dice intact. Depending on your luck, you could at this stage have five, four or three dice, for example.

**5** On each successive roll, players continue trying to add points to their scores or eliminate the 'unlucky' dice until all five dice are 'dead' and the game is over.

**6** Whoever has the most points after everyone else has dropped out, wins.

Whatever you roll, try to avoid 2 or 5 in your throw!